FACT AND FAITH

COMPLETE LIST OF VOLUMES PUBLISHED IN THIS SERIES

Each bound in clothette, 1s. net.

1. **First and Last Things.** By H. G. WELLS.
2. **Education.** By HERBERT SPENCER.
3. **The Riddle of the Universe.** By ERNST HAECKEL.
4. **Humanity's Gain from Unbelief.** By CHARLES BRADLAUGH.
5. **On Liberty.** By JOHN STUART MILL.
6. **A Short History of the World.** By H. G. WELLS.
7. **Autobiography of Charles Darwin.**
8. **The Origin of Species.** By CHARLES DARWIN. (6th Copyright edition.)
9. **Twelve Years in a Monastery.** By JOSEPH McCABE.
10. **History of Modern Philosophy.** By A. W. BENN.
11. **Gibbon on Christianity.** Being Chapters XV and XVI of Edward Gibbon's *Decline and Fall of the Roman Empire.*
12. **The Descent of Man.** Part I and the concluding Chapter of Part III. By CHARLES DARWIN.
13. **History of Civilization in England.** By H. T. BUCKLE. Vol. I.
14 & 15. **Anthropology.** By Sir EDWARD B. TYLOR. Two vols.
16. **Iphigenia.** Two plays by EURIPIDES. English version by C. B. BONNER, M.A.
17. **Lectures and Essays.** By THOMAS HENRY HUXLEY.
18. **The Evolution of the Idea of God.** By GRANT ALLEN.
19. **An Agnostic's Apology.** By Sir LESLIE STEPHEN, K.C.B.
20. **The Churches and Modern Thought.** By VIVIAN PHELIPS.
21. **Penguin Island.** By ANATOLE FRANCE.
22. **The Pathetic Fallacy.** By LLEWELYN POWYS.
23. **Historical Trials (a Selection).** By Sir JOHN MACDONELL.
24. **A Short History of Christianity.** By the RT. HON. J. M. ROBERTSON.
25. **The Martyrdom of Man.** By WINWOOD READE.
26. **Head Hunters ; Black, White, and Brown.** By A. C. HADDON.
27. **The Evidence for the Supernatural.** By IVOR LL. TUCKETT.
28. **The City of Dreadful Night, and Other Poems.** By JAMES THOMSON ("B. V.").
29. **In the Beginning.** By PROF. Sir G. ELLIOT SMITH, F.R.S.
30. **Adonis ; A Study in the History of Oriental Religion.** By Sir JAMES G. FRAZER.
31. **Our New Religion.** By the Rt. Hon. H. A. L. FISHER.
32. **On Compromise.** By JOHN VISCOUNT MORLEY, O.M., P.C.
33. **History of the Taxes on Knowledge.** By COLLET DOBSON COLLET.
34. **The Existence of God.** By JOSEPH McCABE.
35. **The Story of the Bible.** By MACLEOD YEARSLEY, F.R.C.S.
36. **Savage Survivals.** By J. HOWARD MOORE.
37. **The Revolt of the Angels.** By ANATOLE FRANCE.
38. **The Outcast.** By WINWOOD READE.
39. **Penalties Upon Opinion.** By HYPATIA BRADLAUGH BONNER.
40. **Oath, Curse, and Blessing.** By E. CRAWLEY.
41. **Fireside Science.** By Sir E. RAY LANKESTER, F.R.S. Prepared by SURGEON REAR-ADMIRAL BEADNELL.
42. **History of Anthropology.** By A. C. HADDON.
43. **The World's Earliest Laws.** By CHILPERIC EDWARDS.
44. **Fact and Faith.** By PROF. J. B. S. HALDANE.
45. **Men of the Dawn.** By DOROTHY DAVISON.
46. **The Mind in the Making.** By JAMES HARVEY ROBINSON.
47. **The Expression of the Emotions in Man and Animals.** By CHARLES DARWIN. Revised and Abridged by SURG. REAR-ADML. BEADNELL.
48. **Psychology for Everyman (and Woman).** By A. E. MANDER.
49. **The Religion of the Open Mind.** By A. GOWANS WHYTE.
50. **Letters on Reasoning.** By JOHN M. ROBERTSON.
51. **The Social Record of Christianity.** By JOSEPH McCABE.
52. **Five Stages of Greek Religion.** By PROF. GILBERT MURRAY.
53. **The Life of Jesus.** By ERNEST RENAN.
54. **Selected Works of Voltaire.** Translated by JOSEPH McCABE.
55. **What Are We to Do with Our Lives ?** By H. G. WELLS.
56. **Do What You Will.** By ALDOUS HUXLEY.
57. **Clearer Thinking ; Logic for Everyman.** By A. E. MANDER.
58. **History of Ancient Philosophy.** By A. W. BENN.
59. **Your Body : How it is Built and How it Works.** By DR. STARK MURRAY.

The Thinker's Library, No. 44.

FACT AND FAITH

BY

J. B. S. HALDANE, F.R.S.

LONDON:

WATTS & CO.,

5 & 6 JOHNSON'S COURT, FLEET STREET, E.C.4

First published in the Thinker's Library, 1934
Second impression, May 1936

Printed and Published in Great Britain by C. A. Watts and Co. Limited,
5 & 6 Johnson's Court, Fleet Street, London, E.C.4

PREFACE

WITH the exception of one reprinted from the *Daily Herald*, all the articles in this book originally appeared in the *Rationalist Annual* during the ten years 1925–1933. Most of them have already been reprinted in *Possible Worlds* and *The Inequality of Man*, and I have to thank Messrs. Chatto and Windus for permission to republish them here.

The majority of these essays are attempts to summarize our knowledge on important questions. Some of them deal with historical problems on which our knowledge is not increasing rapidly. If I had to write them to-day I should not alter them substantially. But our knowledge of the facts of organic and stellar evolution is growing so quickly that articles on these subjects are liable to be out of date before they are written. I have therefore corrected some details in my essays on these topics, and added footnotes indicating the lines on which I should be inclined to alter them if I had to rewrite them.

My philosophical views have also changed, and, unless my brain hardens prematurely, will go on changing for some years to come. For one thing, the progress of physics, by showing that matter does not possess various properties attributed to it by metaphysicians, has rendered Materialism a good deal more plausible than seemed likely even ten years ago. For another, I have begun to assimilate Dialectical Materialism, a doctrine very different from the Mechanistic Materialism of the eighteenth and early nineteenth centuries, and to my mind far more plausible.

But perhaps these essays will be all the more interesting because they mirror the changes in general scientific knowledge and in my own opinions. Both of these are provisional, just because they are based on facts. A single skeleton of a mammal in Silurian rock would wreck the theory of Evolution. A single conclusive miracle or convincing argument for Christianity would send me hurrying to church. I am not so dogmatic as to say with certainty that none of these events will occur. But I am prepared to bet heavily against them, and to order my life on the hypothesis that they will not happen. On the other hand, I am sure that the progress of knowledge will prove me wrong on many points of detail.

Many of the articles in this book are devoted to the criticism of religion. Almost all of them are to some extent anti-religious. I am often asked why I do not stick to my proper business of scientific research, teaching, and popularization, instead of attacking a religion which leaves me free to go my own way.

There are many answers to this question. In the first place, my practice as a scientist is Atheistic. That is to say, when I set up an experiment I assume that no god, angel, or devil is going to interfere with its course; and this assumption has been justified by such success as I have achieved in my professional career. I should therefore be intellectually dishonest if I were not also Atheistic in theory, at least to the extent of disbelieving in supernatural interference in the affairs of the world. And I should be a coward if I did not state my theoretical views in public.

My opponents will, of course, say that many eminent scientists do not believe in supernatural interference, but are staunch upholders of religion. Now, in this book I am not much concerned with the question whether there is in the universe some mind-like principle which does not, as our own minds do, intervene in the course of events by individual acts of will. I do protest emphatically against calling such a principle God. The religions, which after all have priority in the use of that word, invariably teach that God (or a god) does intervene, and the practice of petitionary prayer is based on this theory.

Secondly, I deny that religion leaves me alone. I wish it did. I am writing this on a Sunday. Now, thanks to English infidels an English Sunday is much preferable to a Scottish Sunday. I remember a series of Scottish winter Sundays in Edinburgh during the War. All places of amusement were shut. So were the public-houses. Even the churches were open for only a part of the day. On the other hand, the rather numerous prostitutes who were thus protected from an unfair competition enhanced their other blandishments by the offer of whisky. The ministers delighted their hearers by fulminating against the godless age which left youth with no bulwark against temptation.

In London things are better. Some museums are open, and even a few cinemas in the evening. This is no serious infliction on me. I can often take an afternoon off during the week. But it is a monstrous injustice to men and women who have to work for six days that their opportunities of amusement should be curtailed on the seventh. A day of compulsory rest was appropriate to a population mostly engaged in hard manual labour. In so far as machinery makes work less fatiguing, recreation should take the place of rest. Nevertheless, Protestants still stop " infidels " from playing on Sunday because it is alleged that over three thousand years ago Jehovah told Moses to forbid the Jews from working on Saturdays.

Religion is like that. It endows excerpts from the laws of primitive peoples with an eternal significance, and stands in the way of any attempt to deal with the problem on constructive lines. An unprejudiced society at our stage of economic development could well afford to allow more than one day of leisure in seven, and would certainly do so during periods of unemployment. And our roads, at any rate, would be considerably safer if, as in Russia, the elementary precaution were taken of not releasing everyone from work on the same day. But here I may be doing my countrymen an injustice. It is possible that the cars which block our arterial roads at week-ends are full of devout men and women going to and from country churches, and that they would not leave London on a less Holy Day.

To take another example, my wife was formerly married to a man from whom she could have obtained a divorce had the Majority Report of the Royal Commission on divorce been put into effect. Since this has not been done, on account of opposition by the Romish and Anglican Churches I was compelled to commit adultery in the most formal manner so as to secure my future wife's freedom. As a result of this quaint proceeding carried out in order to conform with the requirements of the law, I was dismissed from my position at Cambridge, and regained it only on appeal. In just the same way, at an earlier date, an unsuccessful attempt had been made to have me removed from Eton for the crime of possessing and distributing R.P.A. Reprints.

But I find controversies of this kind rather amusing. My real complaint is much more serious. Scientific education and religious education are incompatible. The clergy have ceased to interfere with education at the advanced stage with which I am directly concerned, but they have still got control over that of children. This means that the children have to learn about Adam and Noah instead of about Evolution, about David who killed Goliath instead of Koch who killed cholera, about Christ's ascent into heaven instead of Montgolfier's and Wright's. Worse than this, they are taught that it is a virtue to accept statements without adequate evidence, which leaves them a prey to quacks of every kind in later life, and makes it very difficult for them to accept the methods of thought which are successful in science.

Finally, I object to the privileges accorded to religious organizations, for which I have to pay. I don't mind having a church next door to my laboratory, but I think that it should be rated and taxed on the same scale as the laboratory. If people want religious services, they should be prepared to pay for them as they do for scientific lectures.

And I do not forget my army experiences. Not only was I forced to attend church parades, though I soon managed to wangle my way out of them, but I was compelled to register as a member of some religion. I do not think that clergymen should be allowed to insult wounded soldiers, as one insulted me, by labelling them as members of a religion to which they do not adhere. All I could do was to go the round of the permitted religions, ending up as a Jew, after making sure that there was no rabbi in the neighbourhood.

Even so I should be inclined to take little part in the controversy, were it not for the constant propaganda to the effect that the conflict between science and religion is over, and that recent scientific developments confirm theology. A few of my scientific colleagues support this propaganda. It is true that their reasons for supporting it cancel out to a considerable extent. Sir James Jeans tells us to believe in God because the universe is so orderly that it must have had an intelligent creator; while Sir

Arthur Eddington says that the orderliness is contributed by our own minds. They certainly cannot both be right, and I have a strong suspicion that both are wrong. Nevertheless, they are both used as pillars of religion, which suggests that its other intellectual props must be even weaker.

Now, most scientific men and women of my acquaintance have no use for religion. But they have very little to say against it, for a quite simple reason. The arguments for religious dogmas seem to them so weak as to be quite uninteresting, and in consequence they tend to neglect the study of religion, which is, after all, a very important social phenomenon.

I happen to be interested in it, partly because of its fascinating history, and partly because, however intellectually discredited, it is a social reality which affects us personally. For these reasons I am proud to think that these essays are being added to the Thinker's Library.

Postscript.—On reading through the proofs of this Preface I strongly advise Messrs. Watts & Co. against publishing it. It contains a reference to what I think is a gross injustice done to soldiers, sailors, and airmen. Now, if any of them read it they may agree with me on this question. In other words, this book may be calculated to promote disaffection among His Majesty's forces, or at least some magistrate may take that view. In this case, if a Bill now before Parliament becomes law, not only are the publishers liable to arrest if it is thought that they are about to sell copies to the forces, but the same applies to buyers.

If the publishers are rash enough to include this Preface, I can only warn those who buy it. If they have a friend or relative in the forces, or if their cook is walking out with a soldier, their safest course will be to tear out the offending passage. By the way, this postscript is not a joke. In several foreign countries men and women are to-day being arrested for reasons considerably less serious than a criticism of military authorities, and it is perfectly possible that our own country will imitate the examples which are being set it. I doubt if any passages in the body of the book are seditious, but it is quite likely that by improvements in our law they may become so. It should therefore be read quickly, while it is still legal to do so.

J. B. S. HALDANE.

April 21, 1934.

CONTENTS

		PAGE
PREFACE	. . . .	v
THE CAUSES OF EVOLUTION	. . . . . .	1
ON SCALES	. . . .	20
SOME DATES	. . . .	26
THE ORIGIN OF LIFE	. . . . . .	37
SOME REFLECTIONS ON MATERIALISM	. . .	50
GOD-MAKERS	. . . .	66
MODERN PHYSICS AND CAUSALITY	. . .	85
IF . . .	. . . .	99
STERILIZATION	. . . .	108

THE CAUSES OF EVOLUTION

THERE is a singularly universal agreement among biologists that Evolution has occurred—that is to say, that the organisms now living are descended from ancestors from whom they differ very considerably. A very few, including a distinguished Jesuit entomologist, try to narrow down its scope, but so far as I know none deny it. To do so it would be necessary either to affirm that fossils were never alive, but created as such, presumably by the devil as stumbling-blocks; or that species were wiped out and their successors created on a slightly fantastic scale. For example, the members of one single genus of sea urchins would have to have been wiped out and replaced by barely distinguishable successors some dozens of times during the course of the deposition of the English chalk. This is a *reductio ad absurdum* of a view which was tenable when only a few groups of extinct organisms belonging to very different epochs were known. But if Evolution is admitted as an historical fact, it can still be explained in many different ways.

The iguanodon has been replaced by the sheep and cow, the Austrian empire by the succession states. Some few people will attribute both these events to the direct intervention of the Almighty, a few others to the mere interaction of atoms according to the laws of physics and chemistry. Most will adopt some intermediate point of view. We have therefore to ask ourselves whether Evolution shows signs of intelligent, or even instinctive, guidance; and, if not, whether it can be explained as the outcome of causes which we can see at work around us, and whose action is fairly intelligible.

Popular ideas of Evolution are greatly biased by the fact that so much stress is laid on the ancestry of such animals as men, horses, and birds, which are, according to human standards of value, superior to their ancestors. We are therefore inclined to regard progress as the rule in Evolution. Actually it is the exception, and for every case of it there are ten of degeneration. It is impossible to define this latter word accurately, but I shall use it to cover cases where an organ or function has been lost without any obvious corresponding gain, and in particular the assumption of a parasitic or sessile mode of life. To take an obvious example, the birds were almost certainly derived from a single ancestral species which achieved flight. This achievement was followed by a huge outbreak of variation which has given us the thousands of bird species alive to-day. The essential step was made once, and once only. But the power of flight has been lost on many different occasions—for example, by the ostrich and its allies, the kiwi, the dodo, the great auk, the penguins, the weka, the kakapo (a flightless parrot), and so on. Only the auk and penguins converted their wings into flippers, and may perhaps be absolved from the stigma of degeneracy. Similarly hundreds of groups have independently taken to parasitism, and in many cases very successfully. On the average, every vertebrate harbours some dozens of parasitic worms, whose remote ancestors were free-living. Blake asked somewhat doubtfully of the tiger :

> Did he who made the lamb make thee ?

The same question applies with equal force to the tapeworm ; and an affirmative answer would clearly postulate a creator whose sense of values could not commend him to the admiration of humanity. But, in spite of this, he might be an intelligent being. Now, it is perhaps the most striking characteristic of an intelligent being that he learns from his mistakes. On the hypothesis of an intelligent guidance of Evolution, we should therefore expect that when a certain type of animal had proved itself a failure by becoming extinct, the experiment of making it would not be tried repeatedly. But this has often happened. Both reptiles and mammals have on numerous occasions given rise to giant clumsy types with from one to six short horns on the head. One remembers Triceratops, Dinoceras, Titanotherium, and others. Not only did they all become extinct, but they did not even, like some other extinct animal types, flourish over very long periods. And the rhinoceros, which represents the same scheme among living animals, was rapidly becoming extinct even before the invention of the rifle. But all these animals were evolved independently. Among the Titanotheres alone eleven distinct lines increased in size, developed horns, and perished.

Two or three such attempts would have convinced an intelligent demiurge of the futility of the process. That particular type of mistake is almost the rule

B

in vertebrate evolution. Again and again during Mesozoic times great groups of reptiles blossomed out into an inordinate increase of bulk, a wild exuberance of scale and spine, which invariably ended in their extinction. They doubtless enjoyed the satisfaction of squashing a number of our own ancestors and those of the existing reptilian groups, who seem to have been relatively small and meek creatures.

It would seem, then, that there is no need to postulate a directive agency at all resembling our own minds behind Evolution. The question now remains whether it can be explained by the so far known laws of nature. In the discussion which follows we do not, of course, raise the questions as to how life originated, if it ever did; or how far the existence of an intelligible world implies the presence behind it of a mind.

Darwin recognized two causes for Evolution—namely, the transmission to the descendants of characters acquired by their ancestors during the course of their lives, and selection. He laid more stress on the latter, and was the first to point out its great importance as a cause of Evolution; but, as might be noted by certain anti-Darwinian writers were they to read Chapter I of the *Origin of Species*, he was far from neglecting the former. Nevertheless, thanks in the main to Weismann, the majority of biologists to-day doubt whether acquired characters are transmitted to the offspring. A vast amount of work has been done to demonstrate, if possible, the effect on an organ of its use or disuse throughout many generations. To take a recent example, Payne bred *Drosophila*, a fly which tends to move towards light, in darkness for seventy-five generations. At the end of that time no visible change had occurred in the eyes, and when 1,000 such flies were given the opportunity of moving towards a light no change was found from the normal either in the proportion which moved within a minute, or in the average rate at which they moved. The majority of the experiments on the inheritance of the effects of use and disuse lead to equally negative results. Some of the apparently successful experiments can be explained by selection. For example, wheat taken from Scandinavia to Central Europe and brought back again after some years was found to germinate earlier than its ancestors, and the results were attributed to the effects of earlier germination in a warmer climate. But whereas in Scandinavia the earliest germinating shoots would tend to be nipped by frost, in a warmer climate they would get a start over the later, and be represented in greater numbers in each successive generation. Hence, if there was any inheritable variation in time of sprouting, selection would occur, and the wheat as a whole would sprout earlier.

Nevertheless, a certain number of cases remain which can hardly be explained away in this manner, nor by the transmission of micro-organisms, notably Kammerer's results on salamanders and toads. Until, however, these are repeated, it will be well to suspend judgment, for in the majority of similar cases brought forward in the past, critical repetition has proved fatal to the conclusions drawn from them.

It must be remembered that, however many experiments fail, it is always possible that the effects of use and disuse may be impressed on a species at a rate not susceptible of experimental verification, yet rapid enough to be of importance in geological time. But the acceptance of this principle, and in particular of the corollary that instinct is in part inherited memory, raises difficulties at least as great as it solves. The most perfect and complex instincts are those of the workers of social insect species, such as bees and termites. Now, a worker bee is descended entirely from queens and drones. None, or extremely few, of her ancestors have been workers. If, therefore, memory were inherited, the instincts of workers should slowly alter in such a way that their behaviour came to resemble that of sexual forms, and insect societies should be inherently unstable, whereas in fact they appear to date back for at least twenty million years.

The case for natural selection is far stronger. Let us first be clear what is meant by this phrase. Among the offspring of the same parents variations occur. Some of these are due to accident or disease, and are not transmitted to the next generation; others are inheritable. For example, a single litter of rabbits often contains both coloured and white members. If the whites are bred together, they produce only white young. The coloured will produce a majority like themselves and a proportion of whites. That is to say, both characters are more or less markedly inherited. If now the animals bearing one inheritable character produce, on the whole, more offspring which survive to maturity in the next generation, the proportion of the population bearing that character will tend to increase. The phrase, " Survival of the fittest," is often rather misleading. It is types, and not individuals, that survive. Of two female deer the one which habitually abandons its young on the approach of a beast of prey is likely to outlive one which defends them; but, as the latter will leave more offspring, her type survives, even if she loses her life. Hence, in so far as courage and maternal instinct are inherited they will tend to survive, even if they often lead to the death of the individual. Of course, the fact that nature favours altruistic conduct in certain cases does not mean that biological and moral values are in general the same. As Huxley pointed out long ago, this is by no means the case, and an attempt to equate moral and biological values is a somewhat crude form of nature worship. But that is not to say that the moralist can neglect biological facts.

The assertion is still sometimes made that no one has ever seen natural selection at work. It is therefore, perhaps, worth giving in some detail a case recently described by Harrison. About 1800 a large wood in the Cleveland district of Yorkshire, containing pine and birch, was divided into two by a stretch of heath. In 1885 the pines in one division were replaced by birches, while in the other the birches have been almost entirely ousted by pines. In consequence the moth *Oporabia autumnata*, which inhabits both woods, has been placed in two different environments. In both woods a light and a dark variety occur, but in the pinewood over ninety-six per cent. are dark, in the birchwood only fifteen per cent. This is not due to the direct effect of the environment, for the dark pinewood race became no lighter after feeding the caterpillars on birch trees in captivity for three generations, nor can the light form be darkened by placing this variety on pines. The reason for the difference was discovered on collecting the wings of moths found lying about in the pinewood, whose owners had been eaten by owls, bats, and nightjars. Although there were more than twenty-five living dark moths to each light one, a majority of the wings found were light coloured. The whiter moths which show up against the dark pines are being exterminated, and in a few more years natural selection will have done its work and the pinewood will be inhabited entirely by dark-coloured insects. Naturalists are at last beginning to realize the importance of observations of this kind, but they require a combination of field observations with experiment such as is too rarely made.

Now, it is clear that natural selection can act only when it finds variations to act on. It cannot create them, and critics have therefore objected that it cannot really be said to create a new species. It would follow from this line of reasoning that a sculptor who hews a statue from a block of marble has not really made the statue. He has merely knocked away some chips of stone which happened to be round it ! Natural selection is creative in the same sense as sculpture. It needs living organisms exhibiting inheritable variations as its raw material. It is not responsible for the existence of organisms, but it remains to be shown that without it organisms would display any tendency to evolve.

Of course, if variation is biased in some one direction, a new problem arises. Variation has only been adequately studied during the last twenty years, and it is necessary to digress on the results of this study. Most inheritable variations which have been investigated are transmitted according to Mendel's laws, except that complete dominance is rather rare. That is to say, they are due to the handing on from parent to offspring of a unit which we call a gene, and which is a material structure located at a definite point in the nucleus of the cell, and dividing at each nuclear division. Characters which appear to vary continuously generally prove on analysis to be due to the interaction of a number of such genes. Now, apart from non-inheritable " fluctuations " due to the environment, there are two distinct types of variation. The first and commonest kind is caused by a mere reshuffling of genes. If we mate a black and white rabbit with a blue angora (long-haired) doe, the offspring, if the parents were pure bred, will be black short-haired rabbits; but among their children, if they are mated together, will appear an outburst of variation. Black, blue, black and white, blue and white rabbits will appear, some of each kind having short hair, some long, due to a reshuffling of the genes contributed by the parents. This sort of variation obeys the laws of chance, and selection will be able to pick out only one most favoured combination, say short-haired blue rabbits. Almost all variation in the human race is due to this cause.

But there is another and far rarer kind of variation, known as mutation, which consists in the origin of a new gene. I might breed a million rabbits without getting more than a dozen or so well-marked mutations. But the sort of mutations I should expect would be on more or less familiar

lines. I should not be surprised if I got an outbreak
of hereditary baldness,[1] or came on a new race of
rabbit with pink eyes and a yellow coat, for these
types have arisen in mice; but I should be dumb-
founded if one of my rabbits developed hereditary
horns, and still more so if feathers were to appear.
As a matter of fact, there is a marked parallelism
between the new genes which have arisen in nearly
related species; and this is intelligible because the
structure of their nuclei is similar, and the changes
likely to occur in them are therefore also similar.
New genes appear to arise as the result of accidents
—that is to say, causes which are no doubt determined by the laws of physics, but are no more the
concern of the biologist than those governing the fall
of a chimney-pot, which has been known to alter the
shape of a human head, though not in an inheritable
manner. Mutations have been provoked in mice by
mild injury of the germ plasm with X-rays. The
vast majority of mutations are harmful, resulting in
an impairment of some structure or function, and are
eliminated by natural selection. Others are neutral.
In a fly (*Drosophila melanogaster*) of which some
hundreds of millions have been bred in laboratories
over 400 mutations have occurred, some of them on
many different occasions. Several have yielded
types which are as healthy as the normal under the
artificial conditions of the laboratory. And a few,
in special circumstances, may be more so. For
example, the recessive white-eyed variety, though
considerably less fit than the normal at ordinary
temperatures, is less liable to be killed off by heat than

[1] This has occurred since the article was written

the normal. Actually the fly in question does not live in climates hot enough for this advantage to take effect. It cannot compete with other species which live there. But if it did so the white-eyed variety would be at an advantage compared with the normal type, at least as regards health. It probably would not be fitter on the whole, as its vision is poor. But some other mutant types probably share its tolerance of heat, and if so one of them would probably be favoured by natural selection.

It must be remembered that a mutation which in most circumstances would be disadvantageous may be useful in a special environment. Wingless varieties of normally winged insects are common on small oceanic islands, though by no means universal. Mutations causing loss of wings are also common in the laboratory. It is clear that, after an island has been colonized by a winged insect carried by the wind from an adjoining continent, hereditary loss of wings, if not accompanied by degeneration of other structures, will be of value in preventing its successors from being blown out to sea.

It follows, then, that in mutations of this type we have a means by which sub-species may be formed in nature; and there is strong evidence that they have been so formed. For example, the three varieties of the black rat, which have different geographical distributions, differ from one another by single genes quite similar to those which arise by mutation in the laboratory. But there is no evidence at all that mutations are biased in a direction advantageous to the species. The possibilities of mutation do, however, limit the directions in which a species can evolve. Whether it will do so along any of the lines thus laid open to it depends on natural selection. In some cases, as among flowering plants, a good many species seem to be neither better nor worse off than their ancestors, and therefore to owe their origin primarily to variation. However, a slight change in leaf or flower form is not evolution.

In many cases a change in one character will be of advantage to a species only if some other varies simultaneously in the same direction. This has been used as an argument against natural selection. But, in the first place, although one gene may affect one structure only or mainly, others will modify a whole group. Thus of the genes which alter the wing of the fly *Drosophila* some have little effect elsewhere, some also affect the balancers (rudiments of the second wing pair), others the legs, and so on. A mutation will therefore often be found to kill two birds with one stone, so to speak. Should this be impossible, selection can still work. Suppose it is to the advantage of an animal that two structures, A and B, say bones, should increase together, but that variations in them are inherited independently. We can classify the animals according as the two are of about the average size, greater than the average or about equal to it. So that we get nine classes in all. Those in which the two are unequally developed will be at a disadvantage; only where both are increased will there be any gain. Putting the number of the normal type surviving at one hundred, we should get survival rates somewhat as follows:

	A +	A =	A −
B +	101	98	96
B =	98	100	98
B −	96	98	99

where the figure 101 represents the fact that animals with both A and B increased have a one per cent. better chance of survival than the average. It will be seen that the A — and B — groups will tend to die out, so that both structures will increase in size.

To my mind, the most serious argument against selection on these lines is that it does not explain the origin of interspecific sterility, except where it is due to external causes such as differences of size or breeding-time. It is on these grounds that Bateson, a thorough believer in Evolution, has criticized natural selection. As I have pointed out elsewhere, a difference of a single gene between two animals may cause the production of an excess of one sex on crossing, as occurs in fowl–pheasant and cow–bison crosses : and several such genes may well cause complete sterility.

Moreover, there is a second type of inheritable variation, leading to a change in the chromosome number, which causes inter-varietal sterility, often without a very marked change in external characteristics. This is quite common in plants, less so in animals. Although, therefore, the problem of interspecific sterility is serious, we are already well on the way [1] to solving it.

We must now turn to the palæontological evidence. In a few groups we can trace the course of Evolution in some detail. Thus we know over five thousand species of ammonites, and over two hundred of extinct horses. In the horses advance took place along several parallel lines, only one of which has left

[1] By now all the way in some cases.

living descendants. In each line the toes were gradually reduced from three to one, while the molar teeth increased in length and complexity. When in the past we find two different species competing in the same area, one is usually further on the road towards a single toe, the other towards a long molar. We know that these two characters were of value, because we find fossils in which the thin lateral toes reduced to mere vestiges in the modern horse had been broken during the animal's life, as shown by subsequent healing. We also find that in the more primitive types the teeth were often worn down to the roots, leading to death from starvation. Hence for two species to compete equally, their advantages in these two respects must be balanced, for species combining both advantages, as does the modern horse, would oust those possessing one only. Evolution, in the cases where the evidence is most complete, is known to have been very gradual. Such large changes as those produced by most genes so far studied were rare in Evolution. This is natural enough. Geneticists have concentrated their attention on genes which produce striking effects. Now, however, that they are beginning to look for those causing very small effects only, and often apparently continuous variation, they are finding them.

A more serious objection is that rudimentary characters sometimes appear which can be of no use to their owners, but only become so on further development some thousands of years later. This is almost certainly true, and is at first sight fatal to the selection hypothesis. But it can be met along several lines. A change in one organ, as Darwin pointed out generally carries with it a change in others. Hence an increase in the complexity of one molar brought about by natural selection may cause the beginning of a new cusp in its neighbour. This cusp will at first be useless, but as it increases, selection will begin to act on it also, so that the process will gather momentum until we arrive at the extremely complex grinders of the elephant or horse. Moreover, we can trace just the same gradual beginnings of apparently quite useless organs, the excessive skeletal outgrowths which have been the harbingers of extinction in many animal groups, both vertebrate and invertebrate. If we knew more about these creatures' soft parts we could perhaps elucidate these problems. Some light is thrown on them by recent work of Professor Julian S. Huxley and others. They have shown that in certain animals growth of the whole body leads to disproportionate growth of one part. Thus in a group of crabs, whenever the body doubles in weight, the large claw increases three times, until it becomes almost as large as the rest of the animal. Any cause promoting growth of the whole body, therefore, leads to a disproportionate growth of the claw. And such a cause is to be found in competition within the species, more especially the competition between males for females by fighting, as is common among mammals, rather than display, as seems to be the custom with many birds.

Still, the possibility of some deeper underlying cause of Evolution is often suggested by the study of a whole great group, such as the ammonites, which furnish the best available material, for the following reasons. They were sea-beasts, hence their shells were preserved far better than the skeletons of land animals. The number of their known fossil species is nearly double that of living mammals. Their shells tell us of their development, for the whorls formed by the young animal are preserved in the middle of the complete structure. Finally, their history is over. The last of them died in Eocene times, forty million or more years ago. The earliest forms were often not coiled at all, and always had very simple patterns on the sutures between different shell chambers, and their descendants still made these simple patterns in the embryonic stages. In the great ages of ammonites during the first two-thirds of the Mesozoic era the most complex ornamentation was generally made by the adult animal. But as time went on it showed a tendency to slur its work. The most complex patterns were made by the half-grown creatures, and in cretaceous times the adult shells were even uncoiled, as in the very earliest forms. Now, this " second childhood " occurred independently in some scores of different lines of descent, always as a prelude to extinction. In other groups the same phenomenon may be observed, though the stigmata of degeneration are different.

This degenerative process is often described as the old age of a race, but we must remember that this phrase is only a metaphor. Some very obvious explanations for it are as follows.

A step in Evolution in any animal group is followed by an evolutionary advance on the part of their parasites. When our fish ancestors came out of the water they lost their louse-like crustacean parasites, and it was only after some time that insects can have taken their places, and later still that micro-organisms such as those of malaria and typhus were evolved, which pass part of their life-cycle in insects and part in vertebrates. So the apparent degeneration of a group may only mean that Evolution of their enemies has caught up with their own. Again, specialization, while it leads to temporary prosperity, exposes a species to extinction, or at least to very unfavourable conditions when its environment alters. A small change of climate will lead to a disappearance of forests over a wide area, and with them of most of the animals highly adapted to life in them, such as squirrels, woodpeckers, wood-eating beetles, and so forth. A few, like our own ancestors, adapt themselves to a new environment; but the majority, and all the more highly specialized, die out, the new population of the area being recruited from among the less well-adapted forms. Also, as pointed out above, competition within the species, man included, may lead to results desirable for a few individuals but most undesirable for the species as a whole.

To my mind, the closest analogy to the Evolution of a given group is the history of the art and literature of a civilization. The clumsy primitive forms are replaced by a great variety of types. Different schools arise and decline more or less rapidly. Finally, a period of general decline sets in, characterized by archaism like that of the last ammonites. And it is difficult not to compare some of the fantastic animals of the declining periods of a race with the work of Miss Sitwell, or the clumsy, but impressive, with that of Epstein. The history of an animal group shows no more evidence of planning than does that of a national literature.   But both show orderly sequences which are already pretty capable of explanation.

To sum up, no satisfactory cause of Evolution other than the action of natural selection on fortuitous variations has ever been put forward.   It is by no means clear that natural selection will explain all the facts.   But the other suggested causes are unverified hypotheses, while selection can be observed by those who take sufficient trouble.   Some of the alleged causes, moreover, are difficult to reconcile with the facts of palæontology and genetics.   The evidence as to the earth's age from radio-active minerals shows that about seven hundred million years have elapsed since the first known fossils were laid down, and perhaps twice as long since life appeared on the earth.   This is a larger time than the early supporters of Darwin demanded, and seems long enough to satisfy any quantitative objections as to the slowness of Evolution.   There are qualitative objections, such as those connected with the origin of consciousness.   But consciousness arises anew in every human being.   Its first origin on the earth presents no more and no less mystery than its last.

Finally, no facts definitely irreconcilable with Darwinism have been discovered in the sixty years and more that have elapsed since the formulation of Darwin's views.   Such a fact would be, for example, a convergence in the course of geological time of members of two or more groups to form a single species.   Actually we observe the convergence of forms as we go down and not up a geological series. And there have been quite enough anti-Darwinian Palæontologists to have seized on such a case had it existed. As an explanation of Evolution Darwin's ideas still hold the field to-day, and subsequent work has necessitated less modification of them than of those of his contemporaries in physics and chemistry. Just as physiology has found no case of interference with the order of nature as revealed by physics and chemistry, the study of Evolution has brought to light no principle which cannot be observed in the experience of ordinary life and successfully submitted to the analysis of reason.

C

ON SCALES

" LE silence éternel de ces espaces infinies m'effraie,"
said Pascal, as he looked at the stars and between
them; and his somewhat irrational terror has echoed
down the centuries.

It is fashionable to find the distance of even the
nearest fixed stars inconceivable, and to make no
attempt to grapple with the number of atoms in one's
thumbnail. And this habit of mind makes it quite
unnecessarily hard for the plain man to understand
the main results of modern science, many of which
are quite straightforward, but happen to involve
rather large numbers. For Pascal's attitude is neither
scientific nor religious. " I shall soon be above that
fellow," said Sir Thomas More, as he took his last
look at the sun before his execution; and the modern
astronomer views the sun as a rather small but quite
fairly typical star in a particular cluster.

There is no reason to suppose that interstellar
space is infinite. Very probably the whole of space
is finite, and certainly the distances of all the visible
heavenly bodies are within the range of the human
mind. Infinity is the prerogative of mind rather
than of matter. We can reason about it, but we certainly cannot and do not observe it. As for the silence
of interstellar space, one could not live in it, and
hence could not discover whether it is silent or not.
But if one were shut up in a steel box in it, like Jules

Verne's travellers to the moon, one would probably hear fairly frequently (at least in the neighbourhood of a star) the sound made by a minute dust particle moving at enormous speed hitting one's abode.

The average man complains that he cannot imagine the nineteen million million miles which is the unit in modern astronomy when once we leave the solar system, and is called a parsec because the apparent parallax of a star at this distance is a second; in other words, the earth's orbit from a parsec away would subtend an angle of one second, or look as large as a halfpenny at three thousand yards distance. Of course, one cannot imagine a parsec. But one can think of it, and think of it clearly.

For every educated person learns a process which is really of extraordinary difficulty, and involves a stupendous change of scale. That process is map-reading. In ordinary life our practical unit is about a centimetre, or two-fifths of an inch. Rather few of the measurements of every-day life exceed this in accuracy. Now, suppose we look at a map of the world on a globe measuring sixteen inches round the equator, we are using a model on a scale of one in a hundred million (10^{-8}), and the average man learns to understand its meaning and draw practical information from it. An Englishman hears that his son is going to New Zealand, and has only to look at the globe to see that his letters will take longer to arrive than those from his other son in Newfoundland. But although we are at home on this particular scale, of 1,000 kilometres (or about six hundred miles) to a centimetre, as regards the earth, the average person has not yet grasped the fact that on the same scale the sun is a mile off and as large as a church.

Our grandchildren will have learnt to do the opposite mental trick—namely, to be familiar with models on a scale of a hundred million to one. On this scale the atoms of the common elements are represented as less than an inch across, and molecules of fairly complex organic substances as a foot or so long. The electrons in these atoms and the nuclei round which they are believed to circulate would still be too small to be visible, but we could mark out their orbits, just as we can represent railway lines on a map, though only by exaggerating their width. It is doubtful whether a much greater magnification would serve any real purpose. When we come to deal with the events inside the atom the attempt to represent them in space and time breaks down, or at any rate the properties of space and time in very small quantities are so unlike those of common-sense space and time that models are of rather slight value. On the other hand, models of chemical molecules deduced from X-ray analysis of crystals are most reliable guides, and are opening up a new era of chemistry.

Let us now take a second step in the opposite direction, and try to construct a model such that in it the globe will be as much reduced as the earth had been in representing it as the globe. That is to say, our model is to be on a scale of one in ten thousand million million (10^{-16}). This would really show us very little, for not only the earth but its orbit round the sun would be invisibly small; and even the orbit of Neptune would be comfortably contained on a pin's head, which would also represent the size of the largest known star. Unfortunately, however, even on this scale the nearest fixed star would be about four yards away, and only about twenty would be within twenty yards. Light would creep a yard a year, or much more slowly than a snail, though quicker than the growth of many plants !

But a third step in the same direction would probably be illegitimate. If we tried once more to reduce our scale a hundred million times, the farthest known galaxy of stars would be represented only a tenth of an inch away from the sun, and it is at least possible that all the matter in existence could be shown within a sphere of an inch in radius. For the extended theory of relativity makes it highly probable that the universe is finite in space if not in time. In fact, an attempt to make a model on this scale might produce results as misleading as those obtained when by Mercator's projection we try to represent the surface of the earth on a single plane. For a model representing the neighbouring stars we should do better to reduce by a thousand only, which would bring several of them within an inch, while many at least of the spiral nebulæ would be within five miles.

We have seen, then, that we can usefully think of models up to a hundred million times life-size, and down to a scale of about a ten million million millionth. Beyond those limits space does not have the properties demanded of it by common sense, and visual imagination does not help us. We are compelled to plunge into the mathematics of the quantum theory at the small end, of relativity at the big end. But long before that is necessary people are frightened off the attempt to think, apparently by the word " million." This is because it is generally applied to large aggregates like a million pounds or a million years, which we cannot easily imagine, though as a matter of fact a quite ordinary room would hold a hundred million pounds, provided its floor did not give. But we ought to get the million habit by remembering that we wash ourselves daily in a bath containing about ten million drops of water, often walk ten million millimetres during the day, earn several million centimes per year, and very likely own a million halfpence.

It is a pity that outside India no opportunities are presented of seeing a million men and women, for crowds of this size occur only on Hindu religious pilgrimages, and very impressive they are. A crowd of three million may sometimes be seen at the Kumbh Mela, a twelve-yearly festival which, if I remember, will next be held at Allahabad in January, 1942. I can cordially recommend attendance there to any-one who cannot imagine a million. Incidentally, I am informed that participation in it gets one off several million reincarnations.

In science we soon get accustomed to these large numbers. The astronomer switches over merrily enough from measuring stellar distances in kiloparsecs, which take light 3,000 years to travel, to determining its wave length correct to a fraction of an Ångstrom unit, which is a hundred millionth of a centimetre. And there is a certain thrill when the final result of a calculation which has involved hundreds of millions comes out at one or two, when up till the last moment it might apparently have been anything from a million to a millionth, and thus leads to a simple theory. I am thinking, for example, of Eddington's famous calculation as to why stars are no heavier (for none are known more than about a hundred times heavier) than the sun. Starting from the data of atomic physics, he calculated the internal temperatures of the stars; and since radiation exerts a push on matter emitting, absorbing, or reflecting it, he was able to discover what proportion of the weight of a star of given mass was supported by its own radiation. This proportion is negligible for stars much lighter than the sun, but increases to half in a star about five times the sun's weight, while any star much heavier would burst from its own internal radiation. Thus through a wilderness of millions we arrive at a rational explanation of why all stars have about the same weight.

Again, Gorter and Grendel, and Fricke, have shown by quite independent methods that the oily film surrounding a red blood corpuscle is just two molecules thick. Gorter extracted the oil, and spread it out on water in a film only one molecule thick; Fricke measured the electrostatic capacity of the corpuscles by putting blood in a very rapidly alternating electric field. Both used numbers including the five thousand million corpuscles in a cubic centimetre and the six hundred thousand million million million atoms in a gram of hydrogen, but the final answer was " two " in the one case and " one or two " in the other. It is the success of such calculations that makes it impossible for a scientifically trained person not to believe in the numbers on which they are based.

SOME DATES

FIVE hundred years ago the human mind was limited to a tiny patch of space, and the universe must have seemed even smaller after Magellan's men had girdled the earth. The heavenly bodies were known to be distant, but it was not clear that celestial distances were so much greater than terrestrial. So Cassini's proof, in A.D. 1672, that the sun was nearly a hundred million miles away, was at first too shocking a fact for the mind to accept. Only eighty-nine years ago Bessel measured the distance of one of the nearest fixed stars, 700,000 times greater than that of the sun, and to-day Hubble and other astronomers are estimating distances several million times those that staggered our great-grandfathers.

The range of our minds in time is also increasing; but the process has been slower, partly because time is harder to measure than space, and partly because the chronology of the Old Testament is more precise than its astronomy. So when it was admitted that the earth was older than the six or eight thousand years which the Biblical record allowed, scientific men were at first very moderate in their estimates of geological time. Twenty-five years ago geologists and physicists would not admit that the earth could be more than twenty million years old, although the biologists were asking for hundreds of millions for the process of evolution.

In the last generation, however, evidence has accumulated along at least five different lines which allow us to measure the past with complete accuracy for nearly four thousand years, and with tolerable exactitude for over a thousand million. We may conveniently begin with the nearer dates which fall within the range of history. A generation ago the earliest date known with any certainty was that of the first Olympic Games, 776 B.C. Even if the accuracy of the ages of the patriarchs in the book of Genesis was accepted, the length of time between the births of Jacob and David was very uncertain, and the dates fixed by Archbishop Ussher were to that extent at least conjectural.

But there were certain records of eclipses on historic occasions whose dates were known within a few years. Now a total eclipse of the sun visible from any given place is a very rare event; indeed, only five have been visible in any part of the British Isles since A.D. 1433. So if we know the place where the eclipse was total, and the date within a century or so, we can calculate the latter with great accuracy. Every one, for example, has heard of Tweedledum and Tweedledee, whose battle was interrupted by a monstrous crow as big as a tar barrel. The true story of these heroes is as follows. King Alyattes of Lydia, father of the celebrated Crœsus, had been engaged for five years in a war with Cyaxares, king of the Medes. In its sixth year, on May 28, 585 B.C., as we now know, a battle was interrupted by a total eclipse of the sun. The kings not only stopped the battle but accepted mediation. One of the two mediators was no less a person than Nebuchadnezzar, who in the preceding year had destroyed Jerusalem and led its people into captivity. Other eclipses recorded by the Assyrians enable us to date their kings who were contemporary with the kings of Judah and Israel, and incidentally show us that Archbishop Ussher was forty-six years out in his chronology of that period. This is no discredit to the learned prelate, but is highly disgraceful to the publishers who continue to print Bibles containing it, and the clergy who continue to use them. Whoever else may have been inspired, Archbishop Ussher was not, and we need not pay much attention to clergymen who protest their reverence for Scripture and yet continue to use, or permit their flocks to use, Bibles adorned with the conjectures of an Irish divine whose political talents were at least as marked as his intellectual.

Readers of Homer will remember that Odysseus' return to Ithaca was marked by an eclipse of the sun which portended the doom of Penelope's suitors. As early as A.D. 1612 the attempt was made to date the fall of Troy by this means. But it was only in 1925 that Dr. Schoch of Munich, using far more exact tables of the moon's motion, arrived at the startling result that in the year 1178 B.C. there actually was a total eclipse of the sun in or very near to Ithaca at 11.41 a.m. on April 10. Since the track of an eclipse is only 120 miles broad at most and generally less, and Ithaca is only fifteen miles long, the sun has probably not been totally eclipsed in Ithaca since Odysseus' time, or for thousands of years before. Now, the most probable date for the siege of Troy was generally given at about 1200 B.C.,

so presumably both this date and Homer's story of
the eclipse were approximately correct. One need
not suppose that the suitors were actually killed on
the day of the eclipse, but for the hero's return and
the darkening of the sun to become connected in
local tradition, as they apparently were, they must
have occurred within a few years of one another.

The first date which is known with nearly complete certainty is 1915 B.C. We have accurate tables
of the appearances and disappearances of the planets
in the reign of King Ammizaduga, tenth king of the
first dynasty, who reigned in the city of Babylon
from 1922 to 1902 B.C. In the sixth year of his
reign, for example we read on a cuneiform tablet
recently discovered : " In the month Arahsamnu on
the 28th day Venus disappeared in the west (*i.e.* as
an evening star). Three days she tarried in heaven,
and rose in the east on the first day of Kislev." On
the basis of such data as these Father Kugler, a
German Jesuit, and Dr. Fotheringham, of Oxford,
have been able to arrive at the only possible system
of dates which will fit the facts.[1]

It is, indeed, fortunate that King Assurbanipal,
who reigned in Nineveh from 668 to 626 B.C. approximately, was so addicted to astrology as to have copies
made of the observations of predecessors who, when
he lived, were already as remote as are King Penda
of Mercia or the Caliph Ali to-day. The goodness of
the agreement between dates found astronomically
and those derived from lists of Mesopotamian dynasties

---

[1] The earliest dated event is now the total eclipse of the
sun seen at Ur at 11 a.m. on March 8, 2283 B.C., which shortly
preceded its destruction by the Elamites.

has augmented the faith of historians in the latter, and by their use Professor Langdon, of Oxford, has calculated back to about 3357 B.C. as the date of the beginning of the second dynasty in the city of Ur. Unfortunately, the kings who are recorded as having lived before this date are often alleged to have reigned for many centuries. If we allow them lives of a reasonable length, we arrive at a date for the great Mesopotamian flood somewhere between 5000 and 6000 B.C. This event, which is probably historical, though greatly exaggerated, will not be fully explained till Iraq and Armenia have been studied by competent geologists. At this time a good deal of Scandinavia was still covered by an ice-sheet left over from the last glacial epoch, and the same was probably true of Armenia. Noah's flood may well have been due to an abnormal thaw, perhaps accompanied by the bursting out of a lake or lakes pent up behind a glacier or moraine.

For in Scandinavia and Canada the melting ice has left very exact records, which Baron de Geer and his pupils have investigated; 12,000 years ago the whole of Scandinavia was covered by ice. Then the covering of its southern tip began to melt, and each year the thaw water from it deposited a layer of mud. At any given spot a number of such layers may be found wherever a road or railway cutting or a pit allows the examination of the subsoil. The thick layers due to warm years which thawed much ice can easily be identified. As one travels northward each layer is gradually overlaid by fresh ones, and finally disappears. As lately as 9,000 years ago the site of Stockholm was still covered by ice, but now the ice-fields are restricted to high ground. The final 7,000 years in de Geer's calculations were reached by the counting of annual layers of clay laid down in a lake. In Canada the northern ice-sheet probably reached the great lakes less than 20,000 years ago, though here the evidence is less complete. De Geer's counting of the mud bands gives us an idea of the geological time scale. There were four ice ages during the Pleistocene period. The last of them was already waning 20,000 years ago, and, as there were lengthy warm periods between them, the whole Pleistocene period must have lasted for some hundreds of thousands of years, perhaps the best part of a million. Similar bands, if they consist of mud laid down in annual floods, record the work of a great river in Burma in mid-tertiary times during about a million and a half years.

But the principal evidence for the geological time-scale is of a different kind. Uranium and thorium break down into a series of short-lived radio-active elements which end up as lead. If the rate of decay has always been the same as at present, half of any given mass of uranium is transformed in the course of about 4,600,000,000 years. The fixity of this rate may seem a large assumption. But it is justifiable for two reasons. Firstly, no chemical or physical treatment has the slightest effect on it. Secondly, the speed with which α-particles are shot out from radio-active atoms depends on their rate of decay. Now particles of radio-active matter in mica and other rocks are surrounded by definite spheres of discoloration where the α-particles from them have stopped. If the velocity and hence the range of these particles had altered during geological time, these spheres would not be definite. Assuming, then, that the " clocks " have not slowed down or speeded up, one can use them to calculate the age of the rocks in the following way. Many volcanic minerals contain uranium or thorium, but very little lead. However, there is always some lead, and the older the rock, as judged by ordinary geological standards, the more lead is present. From its quantity we can calculate how long the change has been going on. This gives us the following ages for various rocks (B.M. means before man. It does not matter what individual man we consider) :

Eocene (London Clay) . . . 60 million B.M.
Carboniferous (British coal measures) 260–300 million B.M.
Upper Pre-Cambrian . . . 560 million B.M.
Oldest known rock . . about 1,500 million B.M.

These dates may be as much as 10 per cent. out, but can hardly be much more.

That is to say, 60,000,000 years ago our ancestors were mammals, probably not unlike lemurs; 300,000,000 years ago amphibians, somewhat resembling newts or mud-puppies; and 500,000,000 years ago very primitive fish, combining some of the characters of sharks and lampreys. The origin of life on our planet was probably at least a thousand million years ago, so that the record furnished by fossils only refers to less—perhaps much less—than half of the time during which life has existed.

If all the lead in our planet is of radio-active origin, which is rather unlikely, it can hardly be more than eight thousand million years old. Astronomical evidence points to a somewhat smaller age.

As the earth goes round, the moon, and to a less extent the sun, raise tides in the sea. The energy used in raising them comes from the earth's rotation; hence they slow it down and lengthen the day. The moon thus acts as a brake on the earth, and by so doing is pushed onwards in its orbit, and moves further away. If we calculate backwards instead of forwards, we find both the day and the month becoming shorter, until at a sufficiently early date they possessed the same length of about four hours, and the moon was so near to the earth as to be practically touching it. It is fairly clear that the moon is a portion of the earth thrown off as the result of excessive rotation, almost certainly before the earth's crust had solidified. Unfortunately, the frictional effect of the tides depends on its detailed form. At present the main retarding action takes place in the Bering Sea. At a geological epoch characterized by many shallow and partly landlocked seas, tidal friction must have been greater than now, at other times less. So we can only say that the moon was born somewhere about four thousand million years ago; the true figure might be as low as one thousand million or as high as twenty thousand.

But the birth of the moon was only one event in a greater catastrophe. Our sun, after a relatively brief period—probably a few thousand million years or less—of youthful exuberance as a giant star radiating energy at thousands of times its present rate, settled down as a respectable dwarf, which it now is and has been throughout geological time.

For many thousands of millions of years it probably shone as a lonely star unaccompanied by planets.

Then it appears to have passed near to another probably heavier star, which raised tidal waves in it.[1] The detached crests of these waves, or one of them, formed the planets, and it is fairly clear that the moon broke off from the earth within a few years of its formation. So the approximate dating of the moon's birth gives us that of the earth's. This is further confirmed by the eccentricity of Mercury's orbit, which is still far less circular than the earth's, but is gradually settling down towards circularity. It can be calculated that it has not been going round the sun for more than ten, or less than one, thousand million years. Various other lines of evidence converge to a date somewhere between 8,000,000,000 and 1,500,000,000 B.M. for the origin of the solar system. If science continues, we shall arrive at the exact date in the following way. The relative motions of the various "fixed" stars will be determined, and on calculating backwards it will be found that one passed very near to our sun at a certain date in the remote past. The star in question must be very far away by now. It is a wise child that knows its own father, and we shall probably not know ours for thousands, perhaps hundreds of thousands, of years.

It is possible to penetrate still further into the past and to arrive at a very rough date for the origin of the sun. But any such date depends on some particular hypothesis as to the origin of stellar energy, and there are several such hypotheses, leading to very different dates. On the other hand, a number of independent arguments, based on well-ascertained facts, converge to the same date for the origin of the

[1] But see p. 59.

earth. There are, of course, respectable scientific theories, such as the planetesimal, which lead to different conclusions. The reason for rejecting these theories, and the detailed evidence for many of the dates here given, are to be found in such books as Jeffreys' *The Earth* (Cambridge University Press). In a popular exposition it has been necessary to be dogmatic. If I have been so, it is because I consider it improbable that any of the figures I have given are likely to be very seriously upset in the future.

In a few generations it is probable that these dates will meet with general acceptance, and their meaning will gradually penetrate the human imagination. As the earth has lasted for at least a thousand million years in a condition not very unlike the present, it will probably continue habitable for a future period of at least the same order of magnitude, possibly for very much longer. An acceptance of such a future is bound to affect human thought. It will be realized that the things which seem to us most stable—such as human nature and the facts of geography—are really not only changeable, but certain to change. On the other hand, it will be realized that remarkably little change can occur within a lifetime.

Such a world-view leaves room for optimism in the most desperate circumstances, but yet reduces the probable effects of the vastest human efforts to the tiniest dimensions. As it is accepted, people will probably become more and more prone to devote themselves to their own affairs and those of their immediate neighbours. And when they turn their attention to greater things, they will perhaps be less occupied with institutions as ephemeral as nations.

D

They will be more disposed to serve Man than England or America. A just law may outlive the state in which it was made, a scientific discovery the civilization which brought it forth.

And religion will inevitably alter its standpoint, even if some of its fundamental beliefs survive. On a planet more than a thousand million years old it is hard to believe, as do Christians, Jews, Mohammedans, and Buddhists, that the most important event has occurred within the last few thousand years, when it is clear that there were great civilizations before that event. It is equally difficult to doubt that many events as significant for humanity will occur in the future. In that immeasurable future the destiny of humanity dwarfs that of the individual. If our planet was created a few thousand years ago to end a few years or a few thousand years hence, it is conceivable that the main purpose to be worked out on it is the salvation and perfection of individual human beings. No religion which accepts geology can regard such a purpose as anything but subsidiary.

If we define religion as our attitude to the universe as a whole, the new time-scale will make us humbler as individuals but prouder as a race. Our individual lives are the merest spangles of existence. The life of our ancestors goes back for a thousand million years. That of our descendants may last very much longer. And we cannot say with any certainty that it will not endure for ever.

THE ORIGIN OF LIFE

UNTIL about 150 years ago it was generally believed that living beings were constantly arising out of dead matter. Maggots were supposed to be generated spontaneously in decaying meat. In 1668 Redi showed that this did not happen provided insects were carefully excluded. And in 1860 Pasteur extended the proof to the bacteria which he had shown were the cause of putrefaction. It seemed fairly clear that all the living beings known to us originate from other living beings. At the same time Darwin gave a new emotional interest to the problem. It had appeared unimportant that a few worms should originate from mud. But if man was descended from worms, such spontaneous generation acquired a new significance. The origin of life on the earth would have been as casual an affair as the evolution of monkeys into man. Even if the latter stages of man's history were due to natural causes, pride clung to a supernatural, or at least surprising, mode of origin for his ultimate ancestors. So it was with a sigh of relief that a good many men, whom Darwin's arguments had convinced, accepted the conclusion of Pasteur that life can originate only from life. It was possible either to suppose that life had been supernaturally created on earth some millions of years ago, or that it had been brought to earth by a meteorite or by micro-organisms floating through interstellar space. But a large number, perhaps the majority, of biologists, believed, in spite of Pasteur, that at some time in the remote past life had originated on earth from dead matter as the result of natural processes.

The more ardent materialists tried to fill in the details of this process, but without complete success. Oddly enough, the few scientific men who professed idealism agreed with them. For if one can find evidences of mind (in religious terminology the finger of God) in the most ordinary events, even those which go on in the chemical laboratory, one can without much difficulty believe in the origin of life from such processes. Pasteur's work therefore appealed most strongly to those who desired to stress the contrast between mind and matter. For a variety of obscure historical reasons, the Christian Churches have taken this latter point of view. But it should never be forgotten that the early Christians held many views which are now regarded as materialistic. They believed in the resurrection of the body, not the immortality of the soul. St. Paul seems to have attributed consciousness and will to the body. He used a phrase translated in the Revised Version as " the mind of the flesh," and credited the flesh with a capacity for hatred, wrath, and other mental functions. Many modern physiologists hold similar beliefs. But, perhaps unfortunately for Christianity, the Church was captured by a group of very inferior Greek philosophers in the third and fourth centuries A.D. Since that date views as to the relation between mind and body which St. Paul, at least, did not hold, have been regarded as part of Christianity, and have retarded the progress of science.

It is hard to believe that any lapse of time will dim the glory of Pasteur's positive achievements. He published singularly few experimental results. It has even been suggested by a cynic that his entire work would not gain a Doctorate of Philosophy to-day! But every experiment was final. I have never heard of anyone who has repeated any experiment of Pasteur's with a result different from that of the master. Yet his deductions from these experiments were sometimes too sweeping. It is perhaps not quite irrelevant that he worked in his latter years with half a brain. His right cerebral hemisphere had been extensively wrecked by the bursting of an artery when he was only forty-five years old; and the united brain-power of the microbiologists who succeeded him has barely compensated for that accident. Even during his lifetime some of the conclusions which he had drawn from his experimental work were disproved. He had said that alcoholic fermentation was impossible without life. Buchner obtained it with a cell-free and dead extract of yeast. And since his death the gap between life and matter has been greatly narrowed.

When Darwin deduced the animal origin of man a search began for a " missing link " between ourselves and the apes. When Dubois found the bones of Pithecanthropus some comparative anatomists at once proclaimed that they were of animal origin, while others were equally convinced that they were parts of a human skeleton. It is now generally recognized that either party was right, according to the definition of humanity adopted. Pithecanthropus was a creature which might legitimately be described either as a man or an ape, and its existence showed that the distinction between the two was not absolute.

Now the recent study of ultramicroscopic beings has brought up at least one parallel case, that of the bacteriophage, discovered by d'Herelle, who had been to some extent anticipated by Twort. This is the cause of a disease, or, at any rate, abnormality of bacteria. Before the size of the atom was known there was no reason to doubt that

> Big fleas have little fleas
> Upon their backs to bite 'em;
> The little ones have lesser ones,
> And so ad infinitum.

But we now know that this is impossible. Roughly speaking, from the point of view of size, the bacillus is the flea's flea, the bacteriophage the bacillus' flea; but the bacteriophage's flea would be of the dimensions of an atom, and atoms do not behave like fleas. In other words, there are only about as many atoms in a cell as cells in a man. The link between living and dead matter is therefore somewhere between a cell and an atom.

D'Herelle found that certain cultures of bacteria began to swell up and burst until all had disappeared. If such cultures were passed through a filter fine enough to keep out all bacteria, the filtrate could infect fresh bacteria, and so on indefinitely. Though the infective agents cannot be seen with a microscope, they can be counted as follows. If an active filtrate containing bacteriophage be poured over a colony of bacteria on a jelly, the bacteria will all, or almost all, disappear. If it be diluted many thousand times, a few islands of living bacteria survive for some time.

If it be diluted about ten million-fold, the bacteria are destroyed round only a few isolated spots, each representing a single particle of bacteriophage.

Since the bacteriophage multiplies, d'Herelle believes it to be a living organism. Bordet and others have taken an opposite view. It will survive heating and other insults which kill the large majority of organisms, and will multiply only in presence of living bacteria, though it can break up dead ones. Except perhaps in presence of bacteria, it does not use oxygen or display any other signs of life. Bordet and his school therefore regard it as a ferment which breaks up bacteria as our own digestive ferments break up our food, at the same time inducing the disintegrating bacteria to produce more of the same ferment. This is not as fantastic as it sounds, for most cells while dying liberate or activate ferments which digest themselves. But these ferments are certainly feeble when compared with the bacteriophage.

Clearly we are in doubt as to the proper criterion of life. D'Herelle says that the bacteriophage is alive, because, like the flea or the tiger, it can multiply indefinitely at the cost of living beings. His opponents say that it can multiply only as long as its food is alive, whereas the tiger certainly, and the flea probably, can live on dead products of life. They suggest that the bacteriophage is like a book or a work of art, which is constantly being copied by living beings, and is therefore only metaphorically alive, its real life being in its copiers.

The American geneticist Muller has, however, suggested an intermediate view. He compares the bacteriophage to a gene—that is to say, one of the units concerned in heredity. A fully coloured and a spotted dog differ because the latter has in each of its cells one or two of a certain gene, which we know is too small to see with a microscope. Before a cell of a dog divides this gene divides also, so that each of the daughter-cells has one, two, or none according with the number in the parent cell. The ordinary spotted dog is healthy, but a gene common among German dogs causes a roan colour when one is present, while two make the dog nearly white, wall-eyed, and generally deaf, blind, or both. Most of such dogs die young, and the analogy to the bacteriophage is fairly close. The main difference between such a lethal gene, of which many are known, and the bacteriophage, is that the one is only known inside the cell, the other outside. In the present state of our ignorance we may regard the gene either as a tiny organism which can divide in the environment provided by the rest of the cell; or as a bit of machinery which the "living" cell copies at each division The truth is probably somewhere in between these two hypothesis.

Unless a living creature is a piece of dead matter plus a soul (a view which finds little support in modern biology) something of the following kind must be true. A simple organism must consist of parts A, B, C, D, and so on, each of which can multiply only in presence of all, or almost all, of the others. Among these parts are genes, and the bacteriophage is such a part which has got loose. This hypothesis becomes more plausible if we believe in the work of Hauduroy, who finds that the ultramicroscopic particles into which the bacteria have been broken up, and which pass through filters that can stop the bacteria, occasionally grow up again into bacteria after a lapse of several months. He brings evidence to show that such fragments of bacteria may cause disease, and d'Herelle and Peyre claim to have found the ultramicroscopic form of a common staphylococcus, along with bacteriophage, in cancers, and suspect that this combination may be the cause of that disease.

On this view the bacteriophage is a cog, as it were, in the wheel of a life-cycle of many bacteria. The same bacteriophage can act on different species, and is thus, so to say, a spare part which can be fitted into a number of different machines, just as a human diabetic can remain in health when provided with insulin manufactured by a pig. A great many kinds of molecule have been got from cells, and many of them are very efficient when removed from it. One can separate from yeast one of the many tools which it uses in alcoholic fermentation, an enzyme called invertase, and this will break up six times its weight of cane-sugar per second for an indefinite time without wearing out. As it does not form alcohol from the sugar, but only a sticky mixture of other sugars, its use is permitted in the United States in the manufacture of confectionery and cake-icing. But such fragments do not reproduce themselves, though they take part in the assimilation of food by the living cell. No one supposes that they are alive. The bacteriophage is a step beyond the enzyme on the road to life, but it is perhaps an exaggeration to call it fully alive. At about the same stage on the road are the viruses which cause such diseases as smallpox, herpes, and hydrophobia. They can multiply only in living tissue, and pass through filters which stop bacteria.

With these facts in mind we may, I think, legitimately speculate on the origin of life on this planet. Within a few thousand years from its origin it probably cooled down so far as to develop a fairly permanent solid crust. For a long time, however, this crust must have been above the boiling point of water, which condensed only gradually. The primitive atmosphere probably contained little or no oxygen, for our present supply of that gas is only about enough to burn all the coal and other organic remains found below and on the earth's surface. On the other hand, almost all the carbon of these organic substances, and much of the carbon now combined in chalk, limestone, and dolomite, were in the atmosphere as carbon dioxide. Probably a good deal of the nitrogen now in the air was combined with metals as nitride in the earth's crust, so that ammonia was constantly being formed by the action of water. The sun was perhaps slightly brighter than it is now, and as there was no oxygen in the atmosphere, the chemically active ultra-violet rays from the sun were not, as they now are, mainly stopped by ozone (a modified form of oxygen) in the upper atmosphere, and by oxygen itself lower down. They penetrated to the surface of the land and sea, or at least to the clouds.

Now, when ultra-violet light acts on a mixture of water, carbon dioxide, and ammonia, a vast variety of organic substances are made, including sugars and apparently some of the materials from which proteins are built up. This fact has been demonstrated in the laboratory by Baly of Liverpool and his colleagues. In this present world such substances, if left about, decay—that is to say, they are destroyed by micro-organisms. But before the origin of life they must have accumulated till the primitive oceans reached the consistency of hot dilute soup. To-day an organism must trust to luck, skill, or strength to obtain its food. The first precursors of life found food available in considerable quantities, and had no competitors in the struggle for existence. As the primitive atmosphere contained little or no oxygen, they must have obtained the energy which they needed for growth by some other process than oxidation—in fact, by fermentation. For, as Pasteur put it, fermentation is life without oxygen. If this was so, we should expect that high organisms like ourselves would start life as anærobic beings, just as we start as single cells. This is the case. Embryo chicks for the first two or three days after fertilization use very little oxygen, but obtain the energy which they need for growth by fermenting sugar into lactic acid, like the bacteria which turns milk sour. So do various embryo mammals, and in all probability you and I lived mainly by fermentation during the first week of our pre-natal life. The cancer cell behaves in the same way. Warburg has shown that with its embryonic habit of unrestricted growth there goes an embryonic habit of fermentation

The first living or half-living things were probably large molecules synthesized under the influence of the sun's radiation, and only capable of reproduction in the particularly favourable medium in which they originated. Each presumably required a variety of highly specialized molecules before it could reproduce itself, and it depended on chance for a supply of them. This is the case to-day with most viruses, including the bacteriophage, which can grow only in presence of the complicated assortment of molecules found in a living cell.

The unicellular organisms, including bacteria, which were the simplest living things known a generation ago, are far more complicated. They are organisms—that is to say, systems whose parts co-operate. Each part is specialized to a particular chemical function, and prepares chemical molecules suitable for the growth of the other parts. In consequence, the cell as a whole can usually subsist on a few types of molecule, which are transformed within it into the more complex substances needed for the growth of the parts.

The cell consists of numerous hall-living chemical molecules suspended in water and enclosed in an oily film. When the whole sea was a vast chemical laboratory the conditions for the formation of such films must have been relatively favourable; but for all that life may have remained in the virus stage for many millions of years before a suitable assemblage of elementary units was brought together in the first cell. There must have been many failures, but the first successful cell had plenty of food, and an immense advantage over its competitors.

It is probable that all organisms now alive are descended from one ancestor, for the following reason. Most of our structural molecules are asymmetrical, as shown by the fact that they rotate the plane of polarized light, and often form asymmetrical crystals. But of the two possible types of any such molecule, related to one another like a right and left boot, only one is found throughout living nature. The apparent exceptions to this rule are all small molecules which are not used in the building of the large structures which display the phenomena of life. There is nothing, so far as we can see, in the nature of things to prevent the existence of looking-glass organisms built from molecules which are, so to say, the mirror-images of those in our own bodies. Many of the requisite molecules have already been made in the laboratory. If life had originated independently on several occasions, such organisms would probably exist. As they do not, this event probably occurred only once, or, more probably, the descendants of the first living organism rapidly evolved far enough to overwhelm any later competitors when these arrived on the scene.

As the primitive organisms used up the food-stuffs available in the sea, some of them began to perform in their own bodies the syntheses formerly performed at haphazard by the sunlight, thus ensuring a liberal supply of food. The first plants thus came into existence, living near the surface of the ocean, and making food with the aid of sunlight as do their descendants to-day. It is thought by many biologists that we animals are descended from them. Among the molecules in our own bodies are a number whose structure resembles that of chlorophyll, the green pigment which with the plants have harnessed the sunlight to their needs. We use them for other purposes than the plants—for example, for carrying oxygen—and we do not, of course, know whether they are, so to speak, descendants of chlorophyll or merely cousins. But since the oxygen liberated by the first plants must have killed off most of the other organisms, the former view is the more plausible.

The above conclusions are speculative. They will remain so until living creatures have been synthesized in the bio-chemical laboratory. We are a long way from that goal. It was only this year that Pictet for the first time made cane-sugar artificially. It is doubtful whether any enzyme has been obtained quite pure. Nevertheless, I hope to live to see one made artificially. I do not think I shall behold the synthesis of anything so nearly alive as a bacteriophage or a virus, and I do not suppose that a self-contained organism will be made for centuries. Until that is done the origin of life will remain a subject for speculation. But such speculation is not idle, because it is susceptible of experimental proof or disproof.

Some people will consider it a sufficient refutation of the above theories to say that they are materialistic, and that materialism can be refuted on philosophical grounds. They are no doubt compatible with materialism, but also with other philosophical tenets. The facts are, after all, fairly plain. Just as we know of sight only in connection with a particular kind of material system called the eye, so we know only of life in connection with certain arrangements of matter, of which the biochemist can give a good, but far from complete, account. The question at issue is : " How did the first such system on this planet originate ? " This is an historical problem to which

I have given a very tentative answer on the not unreasonable hypothesis that a thousand million years ago matter obeyed the same laws that it does to-day.

This answer is compatible, for example, with the view that pre-existent mind or spirit can associate itself with certain kinds of matter. If so, we are left with the mystery as to why mind has so marked a preference for a particular type of colloidal organic substances. Personally I regard all attempts to describe the relation of mind to matter as rather clumsy metaphors.[1] The biochemist knows no more, and no less, about this question than anyone else. His ignorance disqualifies him no more than the historian or the geologist from attempting to solve an historical problem.

[1] I think that in view of recent developments in physics and cerebral physiology this statement is over-emphatic.

SOME REFLECTIONS ON MATERIALISM

LOOKERS-ON often see the best of a game. Materialists of a philosophical bent are commonly too occupied in argument with their opponents to draw the logical deductions from their own position. I am not myself a Materialist, but for the above reason I feel that Materialists often fail to do themselves justice. And it is futile either to deny the importance of Materialism or the large element of truth which it contains. It has been pretty completely successful in astronomy, physics, and chemistry. In biology I do not think that any facts inconsistent with it have been discovered. Nevertheless, the biologist must take cognizance of facts (such as the unity of the organism) which have not yet been fully explained on Materialistic lines, and perhaps never will be. In the field of history, both theoretical and practical, Materialism has met with a considerable measure of success in the hands of Marx, Engels, Lenin, and their disciples.

Moreover, Lenin's success as a practical historian— that is, a maker of history—has made Materialism the official creed of the Union of Socialist Soviet Republics. This body may, of course, collapse on economic grounds; but such an eventuality seems far less likely to-day than it did six or even three years ago. Hence Materialism will probably be adopted by a large section of the human race, though most of them will presumably no more be consistent Materialists than their ancestors were consistent Christians.

I am not myself a Materialist because, if Materialism is true, it seems to me that we cannot know that it is true. If my opinions are the result of the chemical processes going on in my brain, they are determined by the laws of chemistry, not those of logic. If I believe that I am writing with real ink on real paper (for, as I write on subjects other than pure science almost entirely in railway trains, I do not use a type-writer), I have no guarantee that this is true. I can only say that the chemical processes associated with that belief increase the probable duration of my brain. And various illusions may have this effect. Unless the chemical processes associated with a belief in transubstantiation went on in the brains of my ancestors between about 1400 and 1550 A.D., these brains were liable to be rapidly oxidized at a high temperature. During the next century, however, the chemical processes associated with disbelief in transubstantiation had a similar survival value. But transubstantiation, if it was true before the Reformation, did not cease to be so on account of Luther and Calvin. To put the matter in another way, if a super-biochemist made a working model of me, atom for atom, this robot would, on a Material-istic view, have all my memories. This may be the case, but if so no knowledge is possible.[1]

Most of the other arguments against Materialism seem to me fairly worthless. Materialists are no

[1] I do not now find this argument as convincing as I did when I wrote it.

E

worse morally than other people. They need not disbelieve in morality. If matter can produce consciousness and truth as by-products, why should it not produce moral obligations? They need not be Atheists, though they generally are. But some Jews and Christians, not to speak of Edgar Allan Poe, have regarded God as a fine type of matter pervading the grosser kinds; and some Atheists, such as the late Dr. MacTaggart, have regarded all so-called material objects as mind in masquerade.

Most people's only serious objection to Materialism is simply that they find it an unpleasant idea. Obviously, however, the pleasantness of an idea is no evidence for its truth, nor *vice versa*. Many of the objections to it on this ground are, moreover, quite unfounded. For example, it is generally supposed to be incompatible with a belief in eternal life for the human individual, whereas, as a matter of fact, it probably implies eternal life, as we shall see later.

At the present time it is being attacked by physicists from two points of view. Ordinary physical observation strongly suggests that every event has a cause. But modern atomic physics does not require this principle, and it is a sound rule in science not to invoke unnecessary principles. The reason for the impasse may be illustrated by a simple case. If we have a large number of " excited " atoms—*i.e.* atoms with more internal energy than they can keep permanently—we can show that, under given conditions, half of them will give up the extra energy within a certain time, say a thousand millionth of a second. If, for example, the excited atoms are sodium atoms, as when we throw salt into the fire, most of the extra energy comes off according to definite laws in the characteristic yellow light. But we cannot tell what an individual atom will do; we can only state the probability that it will do something within a given time. This leads to substantial certainty when we are concerned with large numbers of atoms.

For example, there are about 10^{19} (ten trillion) atoms in a pin's head. Suppose that its physical behaviour is predicted by the laws of physics on the basis that just half the atoms in it will undergo a given process, the chance that one atom in a million will behave in an unexpected manner is rather less than the chance that a hundred thousand bridge deals running, after thorough shuffling, will give each player one suit and only one. In other words, such an event is humanly impossible, though theoretically possible.

However, Eddington, in his Gifford lectures,[1] has suggested the possibility that atomic indeterminism is the same thing as human free-will. In this case the brain is a device for magnifying the undetermined behaviour of atoms to an observable scale. One cannot deny such a possibility. But a biologist can make two comments on it. In the first place, the main task of biology is to explain the fact that living creatures obey laws which cannot be predicted from our present knowledge of physics. We have to explain, for example, why we tend to resemble our parents; and there are plenty of reasons less subtle than indeterminism to explain why this resemblance is not exact. In our search for new kinds of regularity

[1] *The Nature of the Physical World.*

in the behaviour of matter, an unexpected irregularity is a hindrance rather than a help. In the second place, the investigation of human behaviour on scientific lines makes it clear that most of our actions, and in particular most of our moral choices, are rigidly determined.

A different criticism is being urged by Sir James Jeans in a series of papers and lectures.[1] It is essentially similar to Kelvin's argument about the age of the earth. But the time scale is enormously greater, since we now know that, in certain cases at least, matter can be transformed into energy. The argument runs somewhat as follows :—Certain physical processes are irreversible. If we have two cylinders, one full of compressed air and one empty, and connect them, one of two things will happen. If the connection is through a suitable machine, we can make the system do some work. If it is through a tube, the pressure is soon equalized, and when this is done the system can do no more work. The process is, in fact, irreversible. Now, irreversible processes like this are going on all round us. The radiation of heat from the sun is such a process. The source of energy in the sun is probably sufficient to last another million million years or so at a satisfactory rate, but it is not infinite. The same applies to all the other sources of " free energy " in the universe. It will ultimately " run down " to a condition where the temperature of all parts of the universe will be the same. Most, if not all, of this energy will have been dissipated into starlight. A

[1] E.g. *Nature*, 1928, vol. 122, p. 689. It is also very clearly stated in his recent book, *The Universe Around Us*.

great deal, though very possibly not all of its present matter, will have been transformed into starlight; and the process will be irreversible. In a general way the trend of events can be described as an increase of randomness, which is technically called entropy. If we want to diminish the entropy of one part of the universe, as when we separate the iron and oxygen of iron ore, we can do it only by a still greater increase of entropy elsewhere, as when we allow coal and oxygen to unite in a blast furnace.

Working backwards in time, we find more and more of the starlight imprisoned in the matter of stars. We can think backwards in this way for a few million million years, but not for ever. There must have been an initial state in which the universe was, so to say, wound up, and such a state could not be reached from its present condition. Jeans provisionally equates the initial state with creation. Some unique event must be postulated (it is claimed) in the beginning of things, and he leans to a view of the universe not unlike that of the Deists, except that the breach in physical causation took place in a past remoter than our ancestors imagined. This is an unsatisfactory point of view, for, if the laws of physics were once abrogated, there is no reason why they should not be so again, and mediums and faith-healers may be defying them daily. A scientifically adequate theory of the universe must be able, in principle, to explain every state of it as due to a preceding state. It should picture it as having lasted for ever, and capable of lasting for ever as a going concern.

Four main lines of escape offer themselves from

the argument from irreversibility to an uncaused event in the past. It has been suggested that while the stars are running down, other objects—for example, gaseous nebulæ—are " running up," so that, taken as a whole, the universe has always been much as it is now. But attempts to give a physical account of the " running up " process have generally been regarded as failures. Moreover, the present state of the universe agrees very well with the view that it is running down. Thus the stars round us are not moving at random, nor yet according to very definite rules. They behave as if they were on the way from orderly motion towards randomness. Secondly, if the universe is spatially infinite, there is a possible line of escape, for somewhere in infinity indefinitely vast sources of energy can be postulated. But there is strong reason to believe that the universe is not infinite.

The other two lines of escape postulate a reversal of the present tendencies in the universe. At present very large aggregates of matter are impossible, because a very large star would burst as the result of its own heat production. But when the stars have cooled down their clinkers may be able to condense into larger masses. A sufficiently dense system of cold stars rotating round one another would, it is thought, be able to attract and capture vagrant starlight from outer space; for we know that radiation is attracted by matter, though rather feebly. If this is true, the dissipated energy could perhaps be collected again, and a new cycle of stellar evolution begin. I do not think that the theory of general relativity has developed far enough to make a really adequate mathematical examination of this idea possible. We do not know, in particular, whether such an event would lead to a new cycle or merely postpone the onset of the final condition.

The fourth idea is more fantastic, but perhaps more likely to be correct. Imagine the universe to have run down, the temperature being uniform, and all other available forms of energy converted into heat. Probably most of the existing matter would have blazed away into radiation. From the point of view of normal physics, nothing more could ever happen save a blind jostling of radiation and the surviving atoms leading to no appreciable temperature differences, and no motion of large masses. This is a short-sighted view. A resting liquid at uniform temperature appears to be homogeneous, but a small microscopical particle in it is constantly being jostled by neighbouring molecules, and occasionally picks up an unusually large amount of energy and darts across the field of the microscope. Similar phenomena occur in gases near the critical point. They are called fluctuations. The probability of any but a tiny fluctuation is extremely small. Yet no fluctuation, however great, is impossible. The pin's head of which I wrote earlier might spontaneously fly to pieces, using some of its heat energy in the process. But the probability of such an event is vastly less than that of the minute deviation from normality considered earlier.

Nevertheless, the fact remains that when a steady state is reached, any fluctuation, however vast, has a finite probability. Hence, if the universe is finite spatially and contains a finite amount of matter and energy, then in the course of eternity fluctuations of every possible magnitude will occur. I have made [1] a rough calculation from data put forward by Jeans of the time which would be needed before a run-down universe got back to a distribution as improbable as the present as the result of mere chance fluctuation. The time is about $10^{10^{100}}$ years. Perhaps this is an exaggeration, for recent work on stellar and nebular velocities suggests that the universe is not so large as I then assumed. It can, however, hardly be less than $10^{10^{80}}$ years. The number in question is altogether inconceivably vast, although a good Christian would feel himself insulted by the suggestion that his life was limited to such a period. If we wanted to write it down in decimal notation, we should require a great many times more figures than there are atoms in the universe. But that number of years is just the same fraction of Eternity as a second or a century. If an event occurs, on an average, every $10^{10^{100}}$ years, it has already happened an infinite number of times, and will happen an infinite number more. During all but a fraction of eternity of this order of magnitude nothing definite occurs But on a Materialistic view there is no one to be bored by it.

At this point I should like to defend myself against a class of critics who regard such ideas as infinity and

[1] *Nature*, 1928, vol. 122, p. 808.

eternity as nonsensical. When I say that an event has occurred an infinite number of times I mean that with each whole number, 1, 2, 3, and so on, we can relate one past occurrence of that event which is not already related, or labelled, with another number. This is not a very difficult conception, nor does it lead to contradictions.

If this view is correct, we are here as the result of an inconceivably improbable event, and we have no right to postulate it if any less improbable hypothesis will explain our presence. If there are other stars on which intelligent beings are wondering about their origin and destiny, a far smaller and therefore vastly more probable fluctuation would be enough to account for the existence of the human race. Now, according to the theory of its birth developed by Jeans, the solar system originated from the close approach of another star to the sun, which in consequence threw out a filament that condensed into the planets. So near an approach of two stars must be very rare, but not unique. Eddington has calculated that there are probably about 100,000 other planetary systems in the universe. Quite recently, however, Jeffreys [1] has criticized Jeans's theory. He concludes that it would not account for the rotation of the planets. A planet which did not rotate would have only one day per year, and would probably experience such variable temperatures as to make any complicated forms of life impossible. Jeffreys thinks that in order to account for the planetary rotations another star must actually have collided with our sun. The probability of such an event is small compared with

[1] *The Realist*, 1928, vol. i, number 3.

that of a tidal encounter, and on Jeffrey's theory it becomes fairly likely that our solar system, and perhaps our own planet, is the only abode of intelligent life in space. For, even if there are a few other solar systems, their planets may be unavailable for intelligent life on a variety of physical and chemical grounds. And life may originate only under very special circumstances. If this is correct, the fluctuation theory becomes plausible. We have not assumed a more improbable fluctuation than is necessary to account for our being there to marvel at its improbability. If the future progress of astronomy substantiates the uniqueness of our earth, the fluctuation theory will of course gain in likelihood.

We have seen, then, that there is no very valid reason to doubt that there will be material conditions suitable for the development of life like our own through a perhaps unimaginably small, but still finite, fraction of eternity—that is to say, through an infinite time. We do not know enough physics to say whether this means that events reoccur cyclically. If the number of possible configurations of matter and energy is finite, however large, then every configuration will occur and has occurred an infinite number of times. According to the classical physics, the number is not finite—for example, two particles may be at any distance from one another between one and two inches. But some modern developments suggest that only a finite but immense number of distances is possible.

However that may be, it appears probable that only a finite number of animal types is possible. The number is quite large. Let us consider the number of different varieties of one species of fly, *Drosophila melanogaster*, which could be made up by suitable crosses of the varieties at present in existence. There is not enough matter in all the known heavenly bodies, and probably not in the universe, to make one fly of each of the possible kinds simultaneously. The number of possible kinds of man is probably larger; the number of possible organisms less than a mile long is very much larger, but also finite. The reason for regarding the number of types as finite is as follows. Even if the number of possible configurations of living matter is infinite, a living creature acts so as to bring small disturbances in its structure back to its normal. Hence all the various possible types would be reduced by this physiological process to a number which, however large, is finite. Now, in the course of eternity any event with a finite probability must occur an infinite number of times. Hence every human type has occurred already, and will occur again. Of course, the particular kind of material structure called the human body would only be evolved in an infinitesimal fraction of those cycles in which intelligent life occurs. But the fraction would be finite, and that is all that matters.

Now, if the nature of the mind is determined by that of the body (and I think that one may hold a view substantially equivalent to this without being a full-blown Materialist), it follows that every type of human mind has existed an infinite number of times, and will do so. If, then, the mind is determined by the body, Materialism promises something hardly to be distinguished from eternal life. A mind or soul of the same properties as my own has existed during an eternal time in the past, and will exist for an eternal time in the future. Of course, this time is broken up by enormous intervals of non-existence, but it is an infinite time. Such a view differs from the theory of reincarnation in two fundamental respects. In the first place, the mind, though the same in different lives, is new each time, and does not carry over any trace of memory or experience from one to the other. Secondly, there is no reason for supposing it to exist apart from the body of which it is an aspect.

Clearly the most debatable point in the above suggestion is the assumption of identity between two minds. This follows if atoms of the same species are entirely alike except for their relations to the environment. If each one is internally unique, it is obvious that a real physics is impossible. All that we know goes to support the view that there are no internal differences. If so, two similar sets of atoms should determine minds which can be distinguished only by their relations to their surroundings. I must confess that, to me, the prospect of eternal life without memory of my present presents no overwhelming attraction. But yet, if I had the choice between death and complete loss of memory to-morrow, I should choose the latter, if it did not entail mental derangement. Most others would, I think, agree with me; so I presume that continued existence without memory is generally felt to be better than nothing. And if one regards one's personality as possessing some value, there is a certain satisfaction in the thought that in eternity it will be able to develop in all possible environments, and to express itself in all the ways possible to it. Those who have died prematurely will be able, under other conditions, to live out complete lives. Our social organization of to-day is so rudimentary that one feels justified in hoping that our present lives are very poor samples. There is no physical reason, so far as we know, why our humanity should not continue for thousands, perhaps millions, of millions of years more; and it is reasonable to hope that they will, on the whole, be happier than the present or past ages.

If, however, evolution continues, it is likely that in most of our past and future lives you and I have been or will be relatively feeble-minded throwbacks among a more perfect humanity. If so, we shall probably be quite well treated. It is a consoling thought that, even if humanity lasts a million million years and devotes itself entirely to science and mathematics, there will be plenty of quite simple problems still unsolved. For example, there will not have been time and space enough to breed one each of all the theoretically possible varieties of *Drosophila melanogaster*, or to synthesize all the possible organic molecules of a molecular weight less than 10,000. So that I, at least, could find congenial occupations in a world of supermen.

A corollary of the above ideas is that every two persons who meet in the present life have a finite possibility of meeting again, and will therefore do so an infinite number of times, in each case to be parted once more. I believe that they are a logical deduction from thoroughgoing Materialism; and to my own mind the most surprising thing about them is that they have not, to my knowledge, been made before.

They are independent of the precise type of Materialism adopted. I have taken the word in its widest sense, to denote the view that all occurrences depend on phenomena obeying definite mathematical laws, which it is the business of physics to discover. It is quite unimportant whether we call our ultimate reality matter, electric charge, ψ-waves, mind-stuff, neutral stuff, or what not, provided that it obeys laws which can, in principle, be formulated mathematically.

While I think that the theory here put forward is the only logical outcome of Materialism, it may yet have a certain cogency for those who are not Materialists. Though an Agnostic, I am personally much attracted by a modified Hegelian view which regards mind as absolute, and finite minds as contingent, their actual behaviour being regulated by laws of the same general type as regulate other phenomena. On such a view there is nothing unique or permanent about the finite mind, and it may be expected to recur under suitable conditions. Nor is there any reason to doubt that the phenomenal world is eternal. Clearly, however, on such a hypothesis I cannot have so sure and certain a hope of eternal life as if I were a consistent Materialist! The only people who can take no interest in the possibilities which I have suggested are those who regard their souls as absolutely unique and individual. If Christianity is true, they will probably spend eternity in hell (many are called, but few are chosen). According to Buddhism, they have to look forward to a vast number of reincarnations, all, on a balance, unhappy. Some modern creeds purport to be more hopeful. Spiritualists speak of a bright future; but, to judge from such communications as I have received from " spirits," the average spirit is a rather unpleasant type of imbecile. If they do not accept any revelation, it is hard to see what reasons they have to expect anything but annihilation. If, however, I am a natural phenomenon, I see no reason why I should not recur like other natural phenomena.

The speculation put forward in this essay will appear strange. I claim that it is a rational speculation. It is put forward for criticism on rational grounds. I can only add that it grew in my mind during an honest endeavour to shape a view of the universe, and in particular of its remote past and future, which would be consistent with modern physical theory. At the same time, as a geneticist, I was studying the facts available as to the determination of human personality, and it appeared to me as a probable deduction from them that the number of possible personalities, though very large, is finite. If this is the case, and material conditions suitable for life have an infinite duration in time, the other conclusions seem to follow. If they are true, the universe is slightly, but not perhaps very much, better from the human point of view than had previously appeared.

GOD-MAKERS

I AM fond of honorific titles, and I think that life has lost slightly in picturesqueness by their obsolescence. Besides his Majesty the King, his Holiness the Pope, and his Worship the Mayor, I should like to be able to speak of his Ferocity the Major-General, his Velocity the Air-Marshal, and his Impiety the President of the R.P.A. Nevertheless, the most magnificent of all such titles belongs to a past which is not likely to be revived. It occurs in an inscription erected in honour of the Roman emperors Diocletian and Maximian, who are described as " Diis genitis, deorum creatoribus "—that is to say, " Begotten by gods, creators of gods." In those happy days the path to divinity was easier than in our irreligious age. A claim to divine descent might be made on somewhat slender grounds; but, as Diocletian and Maximian named their successors, who, unless deposed during their lifetime, automatically became gods on dying, they could quite legitimately be claimed as god-makers.

It is only when we remember that they were first promulgated in an age of easy deification that we can properly assess the Christian dogmas of the divinity of Christ and the semi-divinity of Mary. At that time there was nothing in such assertions to surprise their pagan hearers, though unbelieving Jews might take a different view; and, as a God, Christ

was clearly an improvement on Claudius or Hadrian.
But if Christianity was probably the best of a number
of competing creeds, it was also the product of an
age when the moral and intellectual levels of the
group of humanity round the Mediterranean were
low—a fact sufficiently attested by their habit of
indiscriminate god-making.

The saints, who perform so many of the minor
functions of divinity in the Catholic scheme, are
rather a mixed lot. Some men and women have
achieved sanctity by virtue, others by hypocrisy,
some again by sheer luck. Of this latter goodly
fellowship none stand higher than St. Protasus and
St. Gervaise. These worthy men (or possibly women,
for, as we shall see, less is known about them than
one might suppose) lived in northern Italy in late
Palæolithic times, some ten to thirty thousand years
ago, and died after doubtless unusually blameless
lives. We do not know whether their beliefs on
unascertainable matters were so coherent as to be
dignified by the name of a religion. But they, or at
least those who buried them, can hardly have believed
that death was the end of Man's individual existence.
For they took a great deal of trouble with corpses.
First, the flesh was removed from the bones. They
may have allowed it to decay, and have dug the
skeleton up again after the lapse of some time. It
is also possible that they stripped it from the bones
soon after death. In this case it was probably eaten,
at least in part, the meal being of a sacramental
character, as still with some primitive peoples. If
so, perhaps we must credit the eaters with religion
of a kind, for the simple and materialistic belief that

F

you can enter into communion with another person by eating him is at the basis of the most powerful religion of to-day.

The skeletons underwent a further treatment. Their heads were removed, and then the various bones were smeared with red ochre. We do not know the reasons for the first operation. Perhaps it was done to prevent the ghosts of the dead from walking. The meaning of the second is more obvious. The blood, as Holy Writ informs us, is the life. So, for a future life future blood is necessary. Ochre is a very good substitute for blood. It is red, and, not being susceptible of decay, may serve as a respiratory pigment during an eternal life. Moreover, recent biochemical research has demonstrated its peculiar suitability as a catalyst for those oxidations which are perhaps even more important in the future life than the present one. For spirit means breath, and the essential function of breathing is to supply oxygen.

Like the owners of other skeletons similarly fortified with red ochre (and many such have been found round Milan), the souls of Gervaise and Protasus, we may hope, chased the aurochs and the wild horse across the happy hunting-grounds, and tracked the woolly rhinoceros to his lair in the Elysian swamps. But faith can work miracles, even on a woolly rhinoceros. Just as it can turn water into wine, and wine into blood (in spite of the fact that œnin, the pigment of grapeskins, unlike chlorophyll, that of leaves, stands in no chemical relationship to hæmoglobin), so it can convert a woolly rhinoceros into a dragon. For in the town hall at Klagenfurt, in Carinthia, stands, or stood till recently, the skull of a woolly rhinoceros. To be more precise, the infidel palæontologist would assign it to *Rhinoceros ticho-rinus*; but the noble knight who slew the dire monster in question said it was a dragon, and he ought to have known. Perhaps he really did kill the last survivor of this species. But more probably it had been extinct for some thousands of years, in which case it is not inconceivable that one of his villeins dug up the skull in his back garden.

Now, if the faith of a quite ordinary knight can transform a woolly rhinoceros into a dragon, why should not that of a particularly holy bishop convert two of its hunters into saints? At any rate, it did so. For a hundred centuries or more the spirits of Gervaise and Protasus hunted their ghostly quarry. But one day their pleasant, if monotonous, existence was sharply interrupted. Two angels appeared, and bore them away, perhaps slightly protesting, to the Christian heaven, where their spears were exchanged for harps and their skins for crowns. As they almost instantly began to work miracles in response to the prayers of the faithful, it appears that they must have adapted themselves to their new conditions more rapidly than might have been expected. Of course, several other cases have been recorded in which souls have gone to an apparently inappro-priate heaven. Such were the souls of the penguins whose baptism by the myopic St. Maël is reported by Anatole France, and that of the Christian knight Donander, which, as Cabell tells us, in that most indecent, blasphemous, and amusing book, *The Silver Stallion*, was transported to Valhalla by an unfor-tunate oversight, and subsequently elevated to Asgard on physiological grounds. And in our own days a respectable German medical officer of health has found himself in the Shinto heaven with Amaterasu and the divine Emperors. Robert Koch, the discoverer of the tubercle and cholera bacilli, and the joint founder with Pasteur of bacteriology, is worshipped as a god in at least one Japanese laboratory. It must at once be admitted that he appears to be quite an efficient god. Japan has produced a number of really excellent bacteriologists. But perhaps in another fifty years bacteriology may no longer be as important in medicine as it is now, and the divine Koch, like older gods, may prove a hindrance to medical progress by diverting effort into ineffective channels.

Spiritual events often have material causes, and we must now trace the mundane events which enriched heaven with its only palæolithic saints. St. Ambrose was one of the first batch of well-born Romans who, after its establishment as the State religion, entered the ministry of the Christian Church as a career. Like myself, he was unbaptized at the age of thirty-four; but, unlike me, he was nominated to a bishopric before the application of that sacrament. He was not only a very able statesman, but a good poet—one of the pioneers of rhyming verse in Latin. In the year A.D. 385 he came into conflict with the secular authorities. The Dowager Empress Justina was an Arian, and demanded the use of a church in Milan for her co-religionists. The history of her conflict with Ambrose has been told by Gibbon in his twenty-seventh chapter. I shall not attempt to tell it again in detail.

Ambrose's tactics resembled those of Mr. Gandhi to-day. While comparing the Empress to Jezebel and Herodias, he affected to deplore the rioting to which his language inevitably led. His methods were successful. The imperial court left Milan, and promulgated an edict of toleration for Arianism. The saint's protest against this tyrannical law led to a sentence of banishment. He blockaded himself in the cathedral with a pious bodyguard, including St. Augustine's mother, who kept up their spirits by singing his newly invented rhyming hymns, which brought frequent tears to the eyes of the future St. Augustine, who had recently been baptized.

During the siege, in response to a vision, he dug for the bones of Gervaise and Protasus. They were found under a church floor, and it was revealed to St. Ambrose that they had suffered martyrdom as Christians under Nero. The multitude were impressed not only by the miraculous freshness of the respiratory pigment of the martyrs, but by the large size of their bones. The Cro-Magnon race, to which the martyrs probably belonged, were, of course, very tall. The bones were carried with due pomp to the Ambrosian basilica. On the way a number of demons were expelled from lunatics, and a man called Severus, who had been blind for some years, was cured on touching the bier of the saints. St. Augustine was in Milan at the time, and records these miracles, which were entirely successful in reinforcing the effect of the hymns. The soldiers did not dare to risk the bloodshed which would have been necessary to effect the capture of St. Ambrose. Shortly afterwards the edict of toleration in favour of the Arians was withdrawn, and the illustrious examples of Gervaise and Protasus did much to confirm the general belief in the efficacy of relics. It only remains to add that twenty-four years after the discovery of the palæolithic saints Rome was sacked by the Arian Goths. This time the trinitarian saints were unable to rise to the occasion. Alaric was made of different stuff from Justina.

But saints are, after all, not gods; and a similar story, though involving a different red pigment, comes down to us from an age nearer to our own. At the Last Supper Jesus is reported to have said of the bread and wine : " Take, eat; this is my body," and " This is my blood of the New Testament, which is shed for many."

Personally, I am not one of those who find it probable that Jesus is a mainly mythical figure. A large number of his sayings seem to me to cohere as expressions of a definite and quite human character, which could hardly have been invented by disciples who wished to prove his divinity. He used figurative language about himself, calling himself, for example, the door and the vine. His self-identification with bread and wine is on a par with these utterances. But by a more or less fortuitous chain of events it has been taken much more seriously. One can imagine developments of Christianity in which every church door or every vine was identified with Jesus, as a pious Hindu may identify every cow with Agni. The actual form of the transubstantiation dogma appears to be due to three facts—the type of mystery religion flourishing in the early days of Christianity, the peculiarities of Latin and Greek grammar, and the activities of a particular god-making bacillus, which, besides upholding the views of the Angelic Doctor, St. Thomas Aquinas, founded a college at each of our two older universities.

The importance of sacramental meals in mystery religions has been sufficiently stressed by others. If to-day we find it difficult to imagine how so much emotion could gather round the act of eating, we must remember that the majority of the early Christians were so poor as to have first-hand experience of real hunger. To most of them food must have presented itself not as a source of mildly pleasant sensations, but vividly as a life-giver.

Once Jesus had been identified with the sacramental meal, it was inevitable that some theory of that identity should be developed. The philosophers got busy. The only tools of philosophers, until very recently, were words, and the art of using words correctly was called " logic." In fact, words are well adapted for description and the arousing of emotion, but for many kinds of precise thought other symbols are much better. Russell and Whitehead were perhaps the first philosophers to take this fact seriously. But a perusal of their books makes it clear that even a greatly improved symbolism leaves room for a very comprehensive disagreement on fundamental tenets.

The European languages are characterized by a highly developed system of adjectives. For example, an Arab, instead of describing the Board of the R.P.A. as infidel men, would call them fathers of infidelity; and I gather that a Chinese might also avoid the use of an adjective in a somewhat un-

translatable manner. Now, the philosophy of the
Middle Ages was the work of men who were ignorant
of nature but learned in Latin grammar. Neglecting
the verbs, they tried to describe the universe in terms
of substantives and adjectives, to which they attributed an independent existence under the names of
substances and accidents or attributes. Modern
physicists are engaged in a somewhat similar attempt
to describe it in terms of verbs only, their favourite
verb at the moment being to undulate, or wiggle.
They are not concerned with what wiggles.

The scholastic philosophy, like any other, led to
results calculated to alarm the pious. The soul was
in danger of becoming a mere adjective of the body,
and was therefore relegated to a special category of
" substantial forms," thus rendering it sufficiently
durable to withstand eternal punishment. With
such highly developed attributes, substance might
have disappeared altogether had not a place been
found for it by the genius of St. Thomas Aquinas.
St. Thomas, it is said, was one of the fattest men
who ever lived, and in his latter years could carry
out the ritual of the Mass only at a specially con-
structed concave altar. Hence his capacity for levi-
tation was even more miraculous than that of lighter
saints. In spite of the distance which separated
him, in middle age, from the consecrated elements,
he was able to observe that no perceptible change
occurred when the bread and wine were converted
into the body and blood of Christ. Very well, said
he, in an excellent hymn, most inadequately rendered
in the English hymn book : " Praestet fides supple-
mentum sensuum defectui " (Let faith supplement

the deficiency of the senses). It did. At the critical moment the substance of the bread and wine was converted into God; but, as all the accidents were unaltered, no perceptible difference occurred. Fortunately, he did not draw the full consequences from his theory. For, if no one could notice the difference when a piece of bread is converted into God, it would appear that the converse operation might also be imperceptible, and no one would notice any change if the object of St. Thomas's worship were converted into a wafer or some other inanimate object. It is also interesting to note that, while St. Thomas was a realist about things in general, he anticipated the views of Bishop Berkeley when it came to the consecrated elements. For he believed that their sensible qualities were directly caused and supported by the deity latent in them.

Now, the dogma of transubstantiation, which needed such strange intellectual props, was not merely based, like many theological dogmas, on traditions of past events which had been brooded over by successive generations of the pious. It was grounded on a series of very well-attested miracles. Not only had individual ecstatics seen visions of Jesus in the host, but large numbers of people had seen hosts bleeding. The first of such events which is known to me occurred in England about A.D. 900, in the presence of Archbishop Odo. Among the most famous is the miracle of Bolsena, which is portrayed in Raphael's well-known picture, and converted a priest who doubted transubstantiation. Allowing for a certain amount of exaggeration for the glory of God, I see no reason to disbelieve in these miracles.

Their nature becomes very probable from the way in which they tended to occur in series, especially in Belgium. A " bleeding host " appeared in a certain church. The faithful went to adore it, and fairly soon others appeared in the vicinity. There is very strong reason to suppose that we have to deal with an outbreak of infection of bread by *Bacillus prodigiosus* (the miraculous bacillus), which would naturally be spread by human contacts. This organism grows readily on bread, and produces red patches, which the eye of faith might well take for blood.

The miracle of Bolsena appears to have finally converted Pope Urban IV to the views, not only of St. Thomas, but of his contemporary, St. Juliana of Liége, one of the two women who have initiated important changes in Catholic practice, the other being St. Marie Marguerite Alacocque, the initiator of the cult of the Sacred Heart. St. Juliana had a vision of the moon with a black spot on it, and was told that the moon signified the Church, the spot being the absence of a special cult of Christ's body. As a result of this vision the Bishop of Liége instituted the feast of Corpus Christi, and in 1264 Pope Urban IV, who had been Archdeacon of Liége, made its celebration compulsory throughout Western Europe. The office for the feast was written by St. Thomas Aquinas. In honour of Christ's body a college was founded at Cambridge within the next century, though the corresponding establishment at Oxford dates back only to shortly before the Reformation. There is no record of what St. Juliana said to the angel who told her about the activities of the poet Kit Marlowe, student of Corpus Christi College,

Cambridge. For it appears from the record of his " damnable opinion " that he was a remarkably militant Rationalist, while a spy stated that he was " able to shewe more sound reasons for Atheisme than any devine in Englande is able to geve to prove devinitie." Perhaps, however, such things are kept from the ears of the blessed.

Unfortunately, *Bacillus prodigiosus* did not confine its efforts to inspiring queer metaphysics and founding colleges. If a bleeding host was God's body, any bit of bread which appeared to bleed was a host, presumably stolen and desecrated. Throughout the ages of faith the same incidents re-occurred. A piece of bread in a house started to " bleed." An informer, generally a servant, went to the authorities. The family were tortured, and finally confessed to having stolen or bought a consecrated wafer and run daggers through it. They were then generally burned alive. Such an incident was often a signal for a massacre of Jews, as in the pogrom of 1370, commemorated in the disgusting stained-glass windows of the cathedral of Ste. Gudule at Brussels, and in the French outbreaks of 1290 and 1433. Sometimes the victims were Gentiles, as in the case recorded by Paolo Uccello in a series of panels which were on view at the London exhibition of Italian painting in 1930. Doubtless among them were a few fools who were genuinely celebrating black masses; but the emphasis laid on the blood in contemporary accounts seems to incriminate *Bacillus prodigiosus*. In England the belief in transubstantiation ceased abruptly in the sixteenth century to be part of the law of the land. " Hoc est corpus " became *hocus pocus*. But in

France the attempt to make injuries to consecrated wafers a capital offence, as deicide, was one of the causes of the revolution in 1830.

So much for *Bacillus prodigiosus*, an organism which produced a delusion more serious than many diseases. But this god-making tendency seems to be one of the more unfortunate vices to which the human intellect is subject. We cannot observe a remarkable phenomenon without postulating something behind it. So far, so good; but we then proceed, if we are not careful, to endow that something with a personality, and deduce the oddest ethical implications—for example, that it is wrong to stick knives through certain pieces of bread. The same tendency operates in the sphere of science. A generalization is made from certain facts, and called a Law of Nature. This is then supposed to acquire, in some quite unexplained way, an ethical value, and to become a norm for conduct. Thus Darwin stated, probably quite correctly, that evolution had been mainly due to natural selection—*i.e.* the elimination of certain individuals, called the unfit, in each generation. The obvious comment was : " So much the worse for nature; let us try to control evolution in some other way." But a number of theorists, including even a few second-rate biologists. seem to have regarded it as an excuse for imitating nature. The weak, it was said, should be eliminated in various ways, and various forms of internecine struggle, from war to economic competition, were justified by an appeal to nature, which was only justifiable if nature represented God's unalterable plan—a view which these writers did not generally hold. The fact that

in most civilized communities the poor breed more
quickly than the rich shows that, from a Darwinian
point of view, the poor are on the whole fit and the
rich unfit. To call the rapidly breeding sections of
the community unfit is certainly bad Darwinism.
They may be undesirable, but that is another
matter. To attempt to suppress them in the name
of Darwinism is an example of muddled thinking
arising out of a partial deification of a law of
nature.

Is the god-making tendency ineradicable, or may
we hope that it will gradually die out or be sublimated
into other channels? As long as it goes on there is
very little chance for the development of a rational
ethic based on the observable consequences of our
actions. To answer this question one must consider
the most important grounds for Atheism. Perhaps
the simplest hypothesis about the universe is that it
has been designed by an almighty and intelligent
creator. Darwin showed that much of the apparent
design could be explained otherwise; but there still
remains a group of facts, such as those collected by
L. J. Henderson in *The Fitness of the Environment*,
which are at present more readily conformable with
the design theory than with any other. It is on the
ethical side that Theism has broken down most completely. For an almighty and all-knowing creator
cannot also be all-good. It has only been possible to
believe in all-powerful gods by attributing to them
one or more of the seven deadly sins. The Græco-
Roman gods were at first conceived of as sharing all
man's moral infirmities. Later, as their characters
were idealized, their failure to improve matters here

below was attributed to what was essentially sloth
rather than active cruelty.

With Christianity the deity became more actively
interested in human affairs, and it was necessary to
attribute to him the darker defects of pride and
wrath. His pride was particularly offended by the
attempts of Satan and Adam to become like him,
and his wrath visited the sin of the latter upon his
descendants during thousands of years. A robust
spirit like Thomas Paine could still see justice in the
universe. It is to more delicate minds like that of
Shelley that we look for the development of Atheism
on ethical grounds. The turning-point came, perhaps, when, under the influence of the Utilitarians,
the State set itself to be less cruel than nature or the
hell-filling god of the clergy. We do not condemn
our worst criminals to anything as bad as an in-
operable cancer involving a nerve trunk. Dartmoor,
our nearest equivalent to hell, has its alleviations
and, what is more, a hope of ultimate release. It
became impossible to believe that the creator of the
universe, even of a universe which did not include
hell, was worthy of our moral admiration.

Christianity had, of course, attempted to meet
such a criticism by the doctrine that God had become
a man and suffered with men. This defence is based
on the celebrated hypothesis that two blacks make
a white, known to moralists as the retributive theory
of punishment. The theory that a wrong act de-
serves the infliction of suffering is part of Christian
ethics, and is responsible for any amount of cruelty
even to-day. And the participation of God in human
suffering, while admirable in a finite deity like

Heracles, does not absolve an almighty power from the blame of having created suffering humanity.

Our present-day Theists generally find two ways out of the dilemma. Either suffering is needed to perfect human character, or God is not almighty. The former theory is disproved by the fact that some people who have suffered very little, but have been fortunate in their ancestry and education, have very fine characters. The objection to the second is that it is only in connection with the universe as a whole that there is any intellectual gap to be filled by the postulation of a deity. And a creator could presumably create whatever he or it wanted. The evolution of life on earth can be pretty satisfactorily explained if we make certain assumptions about matter and life. The origin of the heavenly bodies presents greater difficulties, as will be apparent to any reader of Jeans's *The Universe Around Us*. The theory of creation is essentially a refusal to think back beyond a certain time in the past when it becomes difficult to follow the chain of causation. To hold such a belief is, therefore, always an excuse for intellectual laziness, and generally a sign of it. Probably we are waiting for a new Darwin to explain stellar evolution. But meanwhile an almighty deity would at least explain the apparent irreversibility of natural processes, while a finite deity struggling against the imperfections of matter would explain nothing whatever; and I know of no scientific facts which point to the latter hypothesis. Humanity, or any other aggregate of such a kind, may very well take the place of god in an ethical system, but is not a god in any intelligible sense of that term.

Hence, so long as, on the one hand, scientific knowledge is preserved and expanded, and on the other man keeps his ethical standards above those of nature, the prospects for god-makers are by no means as rosy as they were in the past. I do not, however, think that the only alternatives to Theism are Agnosticism or any of the various forms of Materialism, even though I should call myself an Agnostic if forced to classify myself. There is a great deal of evidence that the universe as a whole possesses certain characters in common with the human mind. The Materialist can agree with this statement, as he regards the mind as a special aspect of one small fraction of the universe in physical relation with the rest. The idealist regards our knowledge of mind as knowledge from inside, and therefore more satisfactory than our knowledge of matter. Unfortunately, there is a tendency to identify the absolute— *i.e.* the universe considered in its mind-like aspect— as in some sort an equivalent of God. I cannot see the cogency of this view. The absolute is not a creator, nor a soul animating otherwise inert matter, but just the universe looked at from the most comprehensive possible point of view. It cannot be identified with any of its constituents, though in the opinion of absolute idealists the human mind is more like it than is any other known finite existent.

Such a philosophy does, as a matter of fact, supply a fairly satisfactory emotional substitute for Theism. It leads one to feel at home in the universe, and yet does not lend itself readily to the attribution of supernatural qualities to finite objects or finite events, which is the essence of all religions. Unfortunately, the history of Hinduism shows that it is compatible with religion in some of its least savoury forms. Brahma is the absolute; but, though he, or it, is venerated, he is not the centre of any important cult. Worship is reserved for Vishnu, Siva, and other minor gods and goddesses. For god-making has been carried out on a very large scale in India. But Brahma at least offers the philosophical Hindu an opportunity of " turning his back on heaven," while preserving his piety—a gesture impossible to a European.

If this be taken as a condemnation of absolute idealism, it should be noted that in Spiritualism we have the beginnings of a new religion, which can exist quite apart from any belief in a supreme deity, and often does so on the continent of Europe, though British and American Spiritualists generally preserve a more or less Christian background. Clearly Spiritualism demands scientific investigation, which would disclose remarkable facts, possibly of the type in which Spiritualists believe—more probably concerning the psychology of small groups. As things are, the Spiritualists are engaged in the same early stages of god-making as the primitive races, who are still mainly animists and ancestor worshippers. Unless the process is checked, Spiritualism will presumably evolve into a fully-developed religion, with sacred objects, intolerance, and that vast diversion of effort into fruitless channels which is in some ways the most characteristic feature of the religions.

I notice among many of my Rationalist friends a lack of interest in the history of religions, which is

G

quite natural when one has examined their fully-developed forms and found them unsatisfactory. Nevertheless, the god-making tendency is always with us, and only by a study of its past are we likely to be able to curb its development in the present.

MODERN PHYSICS AND CAUSALITY

UNTIL recently physics, as generally expounded, was based on the idea of causality, or on some idea, such as invariable succession, which leads to exactly the same consequences. It has lately become necessary to modify the idea, and the result has been the usual chorus from anti-scientific quarters that Materialism has broken down, miracles have a firm scientific basis, and so on. As a matter of fact, the position now adopted by advanced physicists is not new. It was adumbrated by Hume, and still more clearly by Karl Pearson in his *Grammar of Science*. As Hume was, and Pearson is, an " Infidel," I hereby caution the faithful against using doctrines so closely akin to theirs as supports for religion.

Modern physics may possibly be moving away from Materialism, but it is certainly a dangerous ground for theologians to build on. An unfortunate American professor of philosophy, F. C. S. Northrop, a disciple of Professor Whitehead, has recently published a work called *Science and First Principles* [1] in which he identifies the " closed universe," which Einstein deduced from the general theory of relativity, with God. Some time before the publication of the book, Friedmann, and after him Lemaître, showed that if the universe had these properties it would expand without limit. In other words, Professor Northrop's

[1] Cambridge University Press, 1931.

god is doomed to swell up and burst. As, however, Professor Northrop had presumably not read Lemaître's paper, this highly original eschatological conclusion escaped him, and his book has doubtless had a considerable sale in quarters where the reconciliation of science and religion is fashionable.

But all this has nothing to do with the problem of causality. The laws of physics, until recently, were stateable in the form that a situation or state of affairs A was necessarily followed by a situation B. Now, a situation never repeats itself exactly, so a law of that kind could be stated accurately only as follows :—If a state of affairs merely differs from A within certain specified limits, it will be succeeded by one only differing from B to less than a specified extent. A weight of one pound two feet distant from the fulcrum of a lever will balance a weight of two pounds one foot distant on the other side. If our estimations of the two lengths and the first weight are correct to one part in a million, the second weight may differ from two pounds by anything up to three parts in a million. The more accurate our observation, the better is our prediction; but because of the inevitable inaccuracies of measurement we could never predict with absolute certainty, even if we were quite sure of the laws of physics. However, these laws, if only for the sake of simplicity of statement, were put in a precise form. And the tacit assumption was made that there was no limit to the possible accuracy of measurement, so that by progress in technique we could reduce the errors of prediction to as small values as we wished.

Heisenberg states that this last assumption is

false. There is an upper limit to the accuracy of all measurement, and the uncertainty becomes very great when we are measuring things as small as atoms or electrons, though it is negligible in ordinary measurements, which involve billions of billions of atoms.

A hypothetical experiment will make this clear. If we are to predict the future path of a particle, whether the moon or an electron, we must know its position and velocity at a certain time. The easiest way is to observe its position at two successive instants. Now, if the particle is very small we might take two successive photographs of it through a microscope with very rapid flashes of light. But there is a limit to the accuracy of microscopic observation set by the wave-length of the light. With visible light we cannot measure distances smaller than about one five thousandth of a millimetre. To do this we must use some radiation of shorter wave-length, such as X-rays, which allow us to measure the distances between atoms in a crystal. Why not, then, use X-rays for our moving particle, and thus determine its position with very great accuracy? There is no objection save this, that a particle which stops X-rays, light, or any other radiation, is deflected out of its path in the process. So the fact that we have observed the particle means that it has been deflected out of its path on two occasions. The shorter the wave-length the bigger the deflection, so we can measure the position accurately only at the price of vagueness about the speed, and conversely. It is as if the speedometer and mileometer of a car were so far apart that one could not look at both simul-

taneously. Since matter shares some of the wave-
like properties of light, it appears that no other
method of measurement would be any better, and no
physicist has been able to suggest a way of avoiding
this uncertainty. It is negligible compared with
other errors when the particle is as big as the moon,
or even sixpence. It is very large for an electron,
so large that when electrons are crowded together,
as in matter, we cannot distinguish one from another,
or attach any experimentally verifiable significance
to the identity of an electron. These difficulties
apply only to prediction, not to the measurement of
past events. We know where our moving electron
was when it was photographed, but not where it
will go next. It does not, of course, follow that
there is no way out of the impasse.

A good many experimental and a few mathematical physicists hope for the invention of some
methods of observation involving principles as new
as were those of microscopy in the seventeenth
century. The majority prefer for the moment to
express the laws of physics in one of two ways.

One may say that, given a system, say a molecule,
in a given state, there is a certain probability that it
will undergo a specified change within a given time.
Thus to take a case from my own work, there is a
roughly even chance that a molecule of the enzyme
catalase, when combined with hydrogen peroxide
and gingered up with a suitable amount of energy,
will break up to yield water and oxygen in the course
of a ten-millionth of a second. But nothing we can
do will alter this probability, or make it into a
certainty.

Or one may give a perfectly unambiguous account of the universe in terms of wave-mechanics. An electron or proton is represented by a train of waves characterized in a particular manner, which interact with other wave trains. But the electron is nowhere in particular. The waves merely determined the probability of finding it in a given place at a given time. Unfortunately, however, we cannot observe the waves directly, or imagine any method of doing so. C. G. Darwin has suggested that the wave-mechanical account of the universe is the true one, and the account of it in terms of particles the work of our minds.

It is obviously far too early to come to any decision on these difficult matters, and the theory is clearly in its infancy. But so many remarkable facts predicted on the basis of wave mechanics have been experimentally verified that there is little doubt that in some form or other that theory has come to stay. Naturally, those who would like to see the scientific method of tackling problems restricted to as narrow limits as possible have welcomed the view that the admitted unpredictability of future events not only implies the breakdown of the principle of causality, but leaves an opening for miracles, psychic intervention, and the like. It cannot be too clearly pointed out that, though we do not know where a given electron, in certain circumstances, will go next, we do know the probability of its going in any given direction, and any spiritual or supernatural guidance applied to electrons would be as much a breach of the laws of the new physics as of the old. It has been suggested, for example, by a physicist that the human nervous system may serve as an amplifier for these atomic events and translate them to a visible scale. To a biologist this seems highly improbable. Bacteria do, as a matter of fact, obey simple laws of probability, like atoms, as regards their death-rates, and probably in other respects. But even protozoa, and still more higher animals, by mere virtue of their size, escape the tyranny of chance almost completely, just as does an insurance company, provided it issues a sufficient number of policies. Evolution has been an escape from chance, not an amplification of chance. Bacteria are killed by heat according to the same law that an unstable chemical compound, or an unstable element, disappears. This seems to be because the destruction of a single molecule entails the death of the whole microbe. Our lives do not depend in this way on single molecules, but on large numbers, and hence the laws by which our death-rates can be predicted are of a quite different type.

The higher organisms, including man, obey laws which cannot at present be reduced to those of physics. They may be irreducible, but there is no reason to doubt that they are laws. My character is different from yours. In my opinion this is due to physical differences in our brains. It may conceivably be due to differences in superimposed souls. I cannot imagine that it is caused by mere chance—or, in other words, not caused at all.

The attempt to bring the detachable soul theory back in that particular manner is only one of a series of rearguard actions which are constantly being fought by the retreating army of religion. To my own mind the formulation of any at all definite theory of the relation between brain and consciousness seems singularly futile, simply because the matter can be investigated by ordinary scientific method when the technique is sufficiently developed. To-day one can run a needle into one's arm near a nerve, connect up through an amplifier with a loudspeaker, and listen in to the nervous impulses going down from brain to hand when one voluntarily bends a finger. Perhaps in less than a century it will be possible in the same kind of way to observe the cerebral processes associated with consciousness. Already records have been made of electrical changes in the brain, but we have as yet no idea whether the changes so far observed are associated with mental processes.

Speculative theories in science are justified if, and only if, observation is impracticable. It is legitimate to speculate about conditions in the centre of the earth or sun because no one can even suggest, much less perfect, a technique for direct observation of these hellish regions.

Nevertheless, we can already say two things about the mind and body relationship. In the first place, we can place a limit to the possible sphere of indeterminism in human conduct. In the second, we can point out that the progress of physics in the last ten years has removed a great many of the objections to Materialism.

The question of indeterminism can be stated fairly simply. Can we get enough information about a man and his environment to predict his future behaviour with high probability? The answer, of

course, is " No." For the present we must leave
that kind of prediction to palmists and astrologers.
These unselfish benefactors of the human race confine
themselves to predicting the future of ordinary
mortals for very moderate fees, when a simple calculation from the horoscope of Mr. Tom Walls would have
enabled them to predict the winner of the Derby
in 1932, and thus secure a considerable fortune. But
we can also frame our question hypothetically. " If
we had enough information, could we predict a man's
conduct successfully ? " The answer is " Probably
yes." The ground for this apparently unscientific
confidence is the study of twins. Suppose that an
intelligent savage takes the view that every radio
loud-speaker contains an imprisoned spirit, which,
according to its own sweet will, discourses on the
domestic troubles of Mrs. Buggins, the truths of
Revealed Religion, or the habits of the bluebottle fly,
we shall most easily dissuade him by predicting its
subjects of conversation from the *Radio Times*. But
if we cannot find that journal we may be able to
convince him as follows :—There is another loud-
speaker next door. He sends a trusted friend there.
When the two sets are tuned in to different wave-
lengths their conduct is quite different. When both
dials point to the same number then both make very
nearly the same noise. Our savage will either adopt
the materialistic explanation or suppose that the
same spirit can be induced to possess several radio
sets at once.

So with twins. About a sixth of all twin pairs are
monozygotic, or, as Galton rather unfortunately
called them, identical twins. They are of the same

sex, resemble one another physically to a great extent, and, if brought up together, behave in a similar way. Their likeness is almost certainly due to the fact that they are produced from the same fertilized egg, and do not merely have the same parents and pre-natal environment, but receive the same assortment of hereditary material from each parent. If they are separated soon after birth, they may behave quite differently, one being more intelligent or more emotionally unstable than the other. But if brought up together till the age of eight at least, their characters are as similar as their faces. If you have studied one, you can safely bet on the behaviour of the other. Lange [1] studied pairs of monozygotic twins of which one was known to be a criminal. Of thirteen such pairs ten were both criminals, and only three pairs contained one criminal and one guiltless or at least undetected member of society. Thus, if a criminal has a monozygotic twin, the chances are about twenty-three out of twenty-six, or eighty-eight per cent., that the twin will be a criminal too. If we allow for the effects of head injuries, the chances are considerably greater.

Now, I do not think any supporter of human indeterminism would take the view that a pair of twins has only one soul if they are brought up together, and two if they are separated at birth. The alternative is that the soul is responsible for twelve per cent. at most of those acts of moral choice which keep us out of jail. Actually this figure is probably far too high. If we allowed for minor differences of environment in twins brought up together, we could

[1] *Crime as Destiny* (Allen and Unwin).

make our prediction far sharper. I think that an extended analysis along the same lines would show that at least ninety-five per cent. of our important ethical decisions fall within the nexus of causality. And there is no evidence that the other five per cent. fall outside it except our own feelings, which are a doubtful guide and, I think, really only suggest that our will is our own and not someone else's. This proposition is, I suppose, denied only by logical believers in Divine Omnipotence, who are rare. So, if science is undermining the belief of certain physicists in causality, it is certainly supporting the same belief as regards biological matters.

And the curious physical facts which Sir Arthur Eddington brings forward in support of indeterminism furnish at least equally good arguments for Materialism. The main objections to Materialism were as follows. Living organisms have a unity which is very hard to explain if they are made of atoms outside one another in space, and influencing one another only as do the various moving parts in a machine. And it is still harder to explain the unity of consciousness (incomplete though it is) as due to the co-operation of a thousand million brain cells, more especially since Lashley has shown that some features in the behaviour of rats do not depend on any single portion of the brain, but are functions of the cerebral cortex as a whole. This difficulty is just as acute even if we attribute mind-like qualities to individual atoms. Nor can we see how, if consciousness is determined by atomic motions, we can ever have logical grounds for believing in the truth of a statement or the rightness of an action.

But now the physicists tell us that we cannot with certainty pin down an atom to a definite position in space. Space is a feature of human perception and a convenience of human thought rather than an absolute reality. Matter—that is to say, things which exist whether we are aware of them or not— remains as real as ever. But it appears that we have been too rash in our statements about it. Space and time are all very well for describing the moon or sixpence, but if we try to give a thoroughgoing description of atoms in terms of them we are led into self-contradiction. Things are not entirely out-side one another, though nearly enough so for most practical purposes until we get down to atomic dimensions. There is nothing mystical in this partial breakdown of individuality. It can be expressed in quantitative terms, and it enables us to predict future events with increased accuracy. In particular it explains the appearance of new properties as the result of chemical change, and has led to the discovery of some very startling chemical facts, notably the fact that hydrogen is a mixture of two gases, which can be separated, and only change over into one another quite slowly.[1]

We are just beginning to apply these ideas to living beings, but it already seems likely that the very large molecules found in living matter allow of the appearance, on an observable scale, of a sort of wholeness which is not evident in ordinary material systems. One can even see, in a very sketchy way,

[1] This has nothing to do with the more recent discovery of " heavy hydrogen." Both the heavy and light kind, and their compound, exist in two states.

how associated with a brain there may be certain physically specifiable occurrences which cannot be located anywhere particular in it, or at any exactly specifiable time. Such occurrences would perhaps serve as physical descriptions of our mental processes, which are not sharply localizable in our heads, and begin and fade out in a rather indefinite manner. And it does not appear to me impossible that such occurrences should be so related to one another, and to external events, as to exhibit characteristics such as truth and purpose. However, while it would seem that Materialism has become vastly more plausible in the last ten years, its proof or disproof depends on the development of cerebral physiology.

The reasoned objections to Materialism, such as are made by such writers as Professor Eddington and my father, Professor J. S. Haldane, are, I think, partly based on a misconception of the meaning of that term. If Materialism means the belief that you can describe the world in terms of matter as envisaged by Lucretius, Galileo, Mill, or Einstein, it is obviously false. Science is not bound by the words of even its greatest men. The Royal Society recognized this fact when it adopted the motto " Nullius in verba." Only the Church is committed to worship of the Word. Now, philosophers are sometimes sure about the properties of matter, and mathematicians reason as if they were so. An experimental scientist is never sure. If he were, he would not make experiments, except to convince his opponents. But this attitude is most unsatisfactory in a teacher of elementary students. So at any moment there exists a body of rather out-of-date science which is dogmatically taught to school-children and under-graduates. It is clear enough that you cannot explain mind in terms of the properties of matter as laid down in text-books of physics. Fortunately for the prospects of Materialism, every physicist knows that the text-book account of matter will not even explain all its own properties, though it will explain most of those which are of immediate practical importance.

Now, Eddington, struck with the fact that large and small material objects of matter, such as stars and atoms, do not obey the rules which were worked out for objects of medium size, is inclined to doubt whether there are any rules at all, or anything to obey them. And he is confident that if there are any rules he can violate some of them whenever he desires by an act of will. J. S. Haldane, rightly insisting on the fact that life cannot be explained in terms of the physics which he learned in his youth, seems to jump to the conclusion that it cannot be explained in terms of physics at all. It would doubt-less be possible so to define physics that this was true. Actually, however, the physicists are now engaged in stating the idea of wholeness, which in a rather vague way was familiar to biologists, in pre-cise mathematical terms. The attempt is as yet incomplete, but it does not involve the abandonment of the essential physical standpoint, that events can be predicted by the use of quantitative reasoning about things which exist whether we know them or not.

There is perhaps a tendency in Rationalist ranks to take the old-style physics too seriously. In so far as that is so they are fair game for Sir Arthur

Eddington and my father. But the most hide-bound believer in the nineteenth-century mechanistic Materialism is some fifteen centuries nearer to truth than a believer in the Apostles' Creed. Science will, of course, revise its cosmology. It will probably adopt a queerer and queerer world-view as time goes on. But if it continues to fulfil its function of enabling man to predict or control events it will never return to a world-view which failed in both these respects.

IF . . . . .

IN a scientific paper one can almost gauge the intellectual honesty of the author by the number of phenomena which he or she leaves unexplained. The historian, with rare exceptions, is expected to explain everything. This happened because King John was a bad man, that because God willed it, and the other because the feudal system had developed an internal contradiction. It is only a great historian who can dare to confess his complete ignorance. That eminent Rationalist, the late Professor Bury, devoted a learned and fascinating book to the collapse of the Western Roman Empire about A.D. 400. He raised the question of why the Western Empire fell when the Eastern survived, and after a very close analysis he put it down to bad luck—in other words, to causes outside the sphere of the historian. If at the critical moment Rome had produced a military leader it would not have been compelled to rely on Stilicho the Goth, and Alaric might have been repulsed from Rome as he was from Constantinople.

This sort of history is encouraging to the lover of speculation like myself. If individuals count, if Cleopatra's nose and Elizabeth's sexual abnormality really diverted the course of history, then we may legitimately re-write it as it might have been. And just because the details of religion depend so much on the ideas of individuals, even if its general lines are

H

determined by economic and social conditions, religious history should be particularly easy to re-write in this way. So it is not unprofitable to con-sider what would have happened if, instead of being murdered in his tent, Aurelian had reigned for as many years as Constantine, and founded a dynasty devoted to the worship of the Unconquered Sun. We must allow for modifications of Mithraism similar to those which occurred in primitive Christianity, and try to put ourselves in the place of a liberal Churchman of to-day—worried, but not overwhelmed, by the advance of science, and eager to make the best of both worlds. Here is what, but for the dagger of Mucapor, we might to-day be reading, or hearing on the Radio :

MITHRAISM AND ITS CRITICS

Twenty, nay even ten, years ago, the intellectual basis of our faith seemed insecure to many honest thinkers. Old Testament critics had carried with them a large body of opinion, even among the clergy, in favour of the theory that the books usually attributed to Zoroaster contained many later interpolations. And the evidence that even the New Testament writings had not always come down to us in their completely original form had shaken the faith of many. But these things did not touch the core of our religion. The writings of Drews in Germany and Robertson in England, which actually cast doubt upon the historicity of Mithras, were a more serious matter. Fortunately this preposterous theory has been completely discredited by such works as the Bishop of Cambridge's *Mithras the Man*, just as the recent excavations in Persia have done so much to verify the miraculous element in Zoroaster's writings.

But it was the advance of science, rather than the criticism of Scripture, which had done most to shake the faith of those who did not realize that there can be no contradiction between science and religion. For every advance of science has served to confirm the truths handed down to us by our Lord and his Apostles. To take a well-known example, every child asks its mother : " Why does the Sun let the clouds hide His face? ", and one of the dualistic heresies of the primitive Church was, of course, based on the idea that the clouds represented an evil power hostile to the Sun. Thanks to science we know to-day that the Sun Himself draws them up from the ocean by His own power.

The Church of England is based on science as embodied in the Copernican Reformation. The discovery that the Sun is the centre of our system gives us a far truer idea of His greatness than the Ptolemaic system still taught by the Roman Church. And the Anglican Church has always welcomed the advance of science, provided that it was true science and not idle speculation. Rationalists (so called) have regarded the execution of Bruno as a blot on our Church, and have claimed him as a martyr of science because he regarded the fixed stars as suns. They forget that Bruno conceived these bodies as each surrounded by planets like the earth—a doctrine clearly destructive of true religion. His execution was not, of course, in keeping with modern views ; however, he was a martyr not of science, but of error.

Now, when the sizes of the fixed stars were ascertained and their spectra observed, it became clear that in certain respects they did resemble the Sun. For many this seemed the beginning of the end. The champions of religion were not always discreet. We must admit that in Norman Lockyer's famous encounter with the Professor of Dogmatic Heliology at the British Association's meeting at Oxford the Professor had the worst of it. Yet men of faith went on in the quiet certainty that with the further progress of knowledge the wise old heliologians would be vindicated. And it was so. We already know that the vast majority of these so-called suns are utterly unfitted to be luminaries surrounded by planets with living, let alone rational, inhabitants. Some are too hot, others too cold. Many are double, many more are variable. A hundred years of careful search has not produced a tittle of evidence that any planetary system save our own exists. The beautiful researches of Sir Jacob Janes, popularized in *The Intelligible Universe*, have shown that another such system could have come into being only by a miracle. And a rationalism which can defend itself only by postulating miracles is not a very redoubtable foe.

It may well be that many of the fixed stars resemble the Sun as a statue, or even a corpse, resembles a man. But they are not the Fathers of living systems, and they are not themselves alive. It is one of the most elementary facts of religious experience that the Sun is full of an intense life, and no one who opens his eyes without bias on a bright summer's day can well escape awareness of it. No fact of religion has been more abundantly confirmed by science than that the Sun is " the Lord and Giver of Life." Not only has

a study of photosynthesis shown that the energy for
the lives of plants and animals is all derived from the
Sun, but opinion is becoming stronger and stronger
that life on our earth originated in organic matter
formed by solar radiation in the primitive atmosphere.
Finally, every year makes it more probable that our
whole earth is only a detached fragment of His body.
Zoroaster has been fully vindicated.

The fantastic cosmogony of Laplace, according to
which the Sun and His planets were evolved out of a
spinning nebula, has gone the way of other such
follies. A little elementary philosophy would have
shown its deluded adherents that order cannot arise
out of chaos. But during the late nineteenth century
certain Oriental religions became temporarily fashionable in " advanced " circles. Hinduism, disguised as
Theosophy, obtained a certain hold. Still more
fantastic was the attempt to bring Christianity into
Europe. This religion had a certain vogue among
the poorer classes of the Roman Empire in the first
centuries of our era, but vanished, with other dark
things, before the rising Sun of Mithraism. Its extraordinary doctrine that the material world had an
immaterial creator, who yet begot a material son,
could have appealed only to lovers of paradox, and
its moral consequences are sufficiently demonstrated
by the fact that it is the official religion of Abyssinia,
the only state where not merely slavery, but slave-
raiding, is still in vogue.

True religion can be built only on the impregnable
rock of Materialism, and we need not be surprised
that one of the most daring of recent attacks on the
divinity of the Sun is to be found, thinly veiled under

a cloud of mathematical formulæ, in *The Internal
Constitution of the Stars*, by the well-known idealist,
Professor Addington.   Throughout the tacit assumption, based on a possibly fortuitous numerical agreement, is made that the Sun is only a star.   And a
star, according to this author, is a mere ball of gas,
a chaos of atoms and electrons flying at random.

Not for the first time the learning of Oxford has
overthrown the speculation of Cambridge.   There
are many who feel that any attempt to probe the
internal constitution of the Sun, even in a spirit of
the deepest reverence, has a flavour of blasphemy.
We cannot share this view.   Religion, we repeat, has
nothing to fear from science.   So firmly is this principle established by history that we can afford to
neglect pronouncements contrary to religion, made in
the name of science, in the certainty that further
research will disprove them.   Professor Mill of Oxford
re-examined Addington's calculations, and disclosed
that they rested on a concealed assumption.   The
Sun, it now seems, has a gaseous envelope, but a core
of incredible density, in which the matter is organized
in a manner to which our earthly experience furnishes
no analogy.   Here, and not in the solar atmosphere,
we find the material conditions for a Divine Life;
and here, by processes beyond the reach of human
understanding, is generated the energy which we later
see as Light.

If the Sun's atmosphere is gaseous, His core is
eminently solid and material.   And the same is true
of Light.   The hideous hypothesis of Young and
Fresnel reduced the Holy Light Itself to vibrations
in an hypothetical ether.   No more than the particle

theory of Newton could this be reconciled with the truths of religion. After being bandied about for a century by scientific dogmatists the wave theory is now being withdrawn with as little noise as practicable. Light has properties like those of waves, others like those of particles; and matter also has properties of both kinds. By faith we have accepted the doctrine that the Sun, Mithras, and the Holy Light are one. In every century there have been scoffers who asked how this was possible. In the nineteenth century, with the progress of astronomy and physics, the number of those scoffers increased. " The Sun," they said, " consists of atoms, His Light of vibrations —how can they be one? " To-day, if still only incompletely, we see how.

Just as the Solar Life is not, and could not be divorced from matter, human life is inseparably bound up with matter of a different kind. Heretical sects have continually toyed with the idea of an immaterial spirit, and during the nineteenth century several eminent scientists had adopted this theory. Their numbers are diminishing, and Sir Oliphant Ledge, who, till recently at any rate, was a champion of the undulatory theory of Light, is perhaps their last survivor. It cannot be too strongly emphasized that our creeds teach the resurrection of the body by the same Solar power which causes the germination of seeds in the spring. They contain no reference to an immaterial soul.

Such is the position to-day. There is not one of the central doctrines of our faith that has not been completely confirmed by science. It is a question whether we should not give this fact a practical

application.   A constant flood of anti-religious teaching is poured out upon our youth in the name of
science.   Has not the time come when this poisonous
propaganda should be taken in hand?   We do not
wish to discourage honest investigation, even of the
most basal doctrines of our religion.   We must protest, however, when the half-baked theories of the
lecture-room are given to the world as firmly established truths.   The theory that the resemblance
between the Sun and the stars is more than superficial
is hinted at in many school text-books.   The time is
come when such books should be withdrawn.   Thank
the Sun, ours is still, at bottom, a Mithraistic country,
and public opinion is ripe for recognition that, in its
own interests, science should be protected against the
dissemination of such errors in its name.

.   .   .   .   .   .

And so on.   We may be quite sure that this sort
of stuff would find a very wide audience, in spite of
the fact that, according to all the evidence, the sun is
a rather ordinary star, with no more claim to be alive
than has a kettle.   One can always find certain
details of a religious myth or doctrine which are supported by contemporary discovery.   The flood seems
to have been an historical event.   It is true that it
did not drown everyone in Mesopotamia, let alone all
mankind except one family.   But any widespread
flood was good enough for Christian apologists.   The
walls of Jericho had fallen down (at least in some
places).   So they must have been brought down by
Joshua's ram's horn band.   Our present astronomical
equations do not work for more than about two
thousand million years back.   So the universe must

have been created at about that date. We cannot
yet predict rainstorms as accurately as eclipses. So
it is legitimate to pray for rain, though superstitious
to bang the crockery when the sun is eclipsed. But
all these amusing details are negligible compared with
the solid fact that centuries of science have produced
no evidence for Divine intervention in the order of
nature, or the existence of a soul detachable from the
human body.

Religion is still parasitic in the interstices of our
knowledge which have not yet been filled. Like bed-
bugs in the cracks of walls and furniture, miracles
lurk in the lacunæ of science. The scientist plasters
up these cracks in our knowledge; the more militant
Rationalist swats the bugs in the open. Both have
their proper sphere, and they should realize that they
are allies.

STERILIZATION

For some time mental defectives have been legally sterilized in certain American States. A very much more drastic law to the same effect came into force in Germany in January 1934. A committee in London is now drafting a report to the Minister of Health in which the sterilization of mental defectives may or may not be recommended.[1]

Adherents of such proposals claim that they would keep out of existence thousands of miserable beings who can neither enjoy life nor help their fellows. Their adversaries describe sterilization as an intolerable interference with liberty, a punishment for no crime, and a completely futile method of dealing with mental defect.

What is sterilization? It is not castration, but an operation that renders intercourse unfruitful—a kind of permanent birth-control. On a man the operation is quite trivial; less painful, on the whole, than drawing a tooth. On a woman it is much more serious, usually involving a week or ten days in bed.

The German law prescribes this operation, with or without the patient's consent and by force if necessary, for men and women afflicted with nine different

[1] The report, which has been published since the above was written, recommends sterilization with the consent of the patient or his parents or guardians. Provided that pressure is not put on the patients, as in the case of John Hill, this seems fairly harmless in the case of men, though not of women.

complaints, if it is to be expected with great probability that the offspring will suffer from the same complaint. The list includes feeble-mindedness, two kinds of insanity, epilepsy, St. Vitus's dance, blindness, deafness, severe physical malformation, and alcoholism.

There are in this list a few types of disease that are very strongly inherited. Thus a man or woman born with the defect called " split hand " or " lobsterclaw " who has only one or two fingers on each hand transmits this defect, on the average, to half his or her children. So do sufferers from one particular type of blindness. But even where heredity is as strong as this, sterilization would often be ineffective. Thus hereditary chorea (St. Vitus's dance) often does not show itself until the victim is forty years old, after which time he or she is not likely to have any more children, so that sterilization would be futile. The only method likely to detect the condition earlier was devised by a professor at Göttingen, who has since been expelled as a Jew and is unlikely to have opportunities to perfect it.

Even where a character is very strongly inherited, a lover of liberty might suggest that compulsory methods should not be tried until it has been shown that no amount of propaganda will persuade the people concerned to abstain from parenthood. But in most cases characters are not at all strongly inherited. This is particularly so with feeble-mindedness. A recent investigation at Birmingham dealt with 345 children, at least one of whose parents had been at a special school for mental defectives. Only 25 of these children were themselves defective, 62 others were backward, and the rest normal or, in nine cases, above the average.

A good deal of mental defect has nothing to do with heredity. One type is caused by injury at birth, another can be cured by administering thyroid gland, and so on. But, even when these are excluded, the majority of defective children are born of normal parents. If all the feeble-minded in England were sterilized to-morrow, it is doubtful whether the number of defectives in the next generation would be cut down by one-tenth. Insanity is even less strongly inherited than feeble-mindedness, though it is easier to detect.

Even so, compulsory sterilization, of men at least, might be desirable if it was certain to be applied with impartial justice. But such justice is impossible in our society as at present constituted in England or America, let alone Germany, where a prison director may propose any prisoner for sterilization, and men and women are imprisoned for qualities that are found admirable in other countries.

Let us see how sterilization actually works in the United States. John Hill was a labourer in the beet sugar industry. He had five children. As they were hungry he stole a number of hams. He was given an indeterminate sentence up to fifteen years' imprisonment. The judge suspended it during his good behaviour, but recommended him to submit to sterilization, which he did. John Hill may have been feeble-minded, but he would not have stolen the hams, and would not have been sterilized, if he had been a rich man.

If voluntary sterilization becomes legal in England,

we must be very sure that magistrates will not be allowed to recommend it as an alternative to imprisonment. The same judge who sentenced John Hill ordered the sterilization of another prisoner, using the words " He has a strain of Negro blood in his veins, and has a lustful and disgusting appearance." Is it likely that German eugenic courts will be completely impartial with regard to race, in view of the fact that the principal German text-book of eugenics preaches the congenital inferiority of various races ?

Perhaps the gravest objection against sterilization is that the propaganda in its favour has blinded many people to other methods of dealing with congenital defects. Many are not due to heredity in the ordinary sense, but to inbreeding. For example, about one in four of all born deaf mutes is the offspring of the two first cousins. Also because a defect is congenital it is not necessarily incurable. Short sight is often strongly inherited. But spectacles are cheap. There are already ways of strengthening some kinds of congenitally weak brains, and others will doubtless be discovered.

Sterilization, for men at least, would probably be justified to-day in the case of a few well-marked physical defects. Its wholesale application is one of the many policies, like compulsory labour, which would be grossly unfair in our present society, but fair in a community where all had equal rights and equal opportunities. When every child has had a fair chance it will be time enough to label the most backward as congenitally weak-minded. But meanwhile the task of dealing with social and economic inequality should come first.

THE RATIONALIST PRESS
ASSOCIATION LIMITED

THE R.P.A., as it is generally styled, consists of some thousands of men and women scattered throughout the world, of many different nationalities, and of very varied social position and economic circumstance. They are pledged to no creed, to no set of dogmas; but they accept the supremacy of Reason, and aim at making this supremacy effectual in the affairs of everyday life.

In the thirty odd years of its existence the R.P.A. has printed and sold more than four million cheap reprints of the works of the great thinkers—Huxley, Darwin, Spencer, Mill, Haeckel, Renan, Paine, Winwood Reade, Lecky, Clodd, Bradlaugh, etc., in addition to hundreds of thousands of copies of new works on Science (particularly Evolution), History, Philosophy, and Biblical Criticism.

Among the Association's publications are two series of cheap books which have achieved a wide popularity. One is the Forum Series, issued at 1s. and 7d., consisting of original works by some of the leading thinkers of the day, including Sir Arthur Keith, Mr. Julian S. Huxley, Hon. John Collier, Dr. C. E. M. Joad, Major Leonard Darwin, Professor Edward Westermarck, etc. The other is the Thinker's Library, which comprises mainly reprints of famous works, attractively produced at one shilling each. Among the titles which have already appeared are Mr. H. G. Wells's *First and Last Things* and *Short History of the World*, Spencer's *Education*, Haeckel's *Riddle of the Universe*, Rt. Hon. J. M. Robertson's *Short History of Christianity*, Sir John Macdonell's *Historical Trials*, Llewelyn Powys's *Pathetic Fallacy*, Sir Leslie Stephen's *Agnostic's Apology*, James Harvey Robinson's *The Mind in the Making*, Darwin's *Origin of Species*, Winwood Reade's *Martyrdom of Man*, Sir J. G. Frazer's *Adonis*, Anatole France's *Penguin Island* and *Revolt of the Angels*, Aldous Huxley's *Do What You Will*, and Professor Gilbert Murray's *Five Stages of Greek Religion*.

The R.P.A. is not satisfied with what it has done. It wants to put within the reach of the leanest purse still more of the fine intellectual product of the ages; it wants to make it possible for every one to satisfy his thirst for knowledge, to know the facts of life.

To carry out these aims the co-operation of Rationalists is essential. If you are in sympathy with its objects, if you appreciate the work it has done in the past and would like to help it to do better work in the future, you should complete the form on the next page and

JOIN THE R.P.A. NOW!

NOTE.—Members are entitled to receive publications of the Association to the full value of their annual subscriptions. Minimum Subscription, 5s.

APPLICATION FOR MEMBERSHIP

To THE SECRETARY, *The Rationalist Press Association Limited,*
Nos. 4–6 Johnson's Court, Fleet Street, London, E.C. 4.

DEAR SIR,

I desire to become a Member [1] of the Rationalist Press Association Limited, and enclose herewith my first annual subscription [2]

of.............................; my Membership to commence with the current year.[3] I agree to abide by the Rules and Regulations of the Association as set forth in the Memorandum and Articles of Association.[4]

Please write in block letters

Name...

[If lady, state whether Mrs. or Miss]

Address ....

....

Occupation...

[Completion Optional]

Date........................... Signature.................................

A Subscriber who does not wish to have his or her name published in the Annual Report or any other subscription list can add here the initials or pseudonym under which the contribution is to be acknowledged.

Initials or Pseudonym...

---

[1] Persons under twenty-one years of age are not eligible for Membership, but may become "Non-member Subscribers."

[2] The minimum subscription is 5s., but it is hoped that those who can afford to subscribe more liberally will do so.

[3] Subscriptions are due in advance on the first of January of each year, so that persons who apply for Membership late in the year should cross out "the current" and substitute "next" if it be not their intention to renew the subscription in the following January. Members joining late in the year, however, are entitled to receive the Association's publications to the full value of their subscriptions.

[4] The Memorandum and Articles of Association, or any desired information, will be forwarded free on application to the Secretary.